Wave goodbye to exam worries with CGP!

It can seem like there's an ocean of info to learn for GCSE Geography.
But never fear, this CGP Workbook will erode your exam troubles...

It's packed with stacks of exam-style questions for every Edexcel A topic
— perfect for making sure you're ready for the real thing.

There's also practice for fieldwork and investigation questions — everything
you need to shore up your knowledge and coast through the exams.

CGP — still the best! ☺

Our sole aim here at CGP is to produce the highest quality books —
carefully written, immaculately presented and dangerously close to being funny.

Then we work our socks off to get them out to you
— at the cheapest possible prices.

Contents

✓ Use the tick boxes to check off the topics you've completed.

Component 2:
The Human Environment

Topic 4 — Changing Cities

Topic 5 — Global Development

Topic 6 — Resource Management

Energy Resource Management

Water Resource Management

Component 3:
Geographical Investigations — Fieldwork and UK Challenges

Geographical Investigations — Fieldwork

Geographical Investigations — UK Challenges

Don't Forget

You don't need to answer all of the questions in Topics 1 and 6 — some of the sections are optional. See page 2 for more details.

Published by CGP

Editors:
Alex Billings, Claire Boulter, Ellen Burton, Katharine Howell, Claire Plowman.

With thanks to Nic Robinson for the proofreading.

With thanks to Emily Smith for copyright research.

ISBN: 978 1 78908 302 6

How to Use this Book

- Hold the book upright, approximately 50 cm from your face, ensuring that the text looks like this, not sıɥʇ. Alternatively, place the book on a horizontal surface (e.g. a table or desk) and sit adjacent to the book, at a distance which doesn't make the text too small to read.
- In case of emergency, press the two halves of the book together firmly in order to close.
- Before attempting to use this book, familiarise yourself with the following safety information:

> The questions are arranged into subjects, so you can get exam practice on exactly the bit of your course that you want.

50

Tropical Rainforests — Sustainable Management

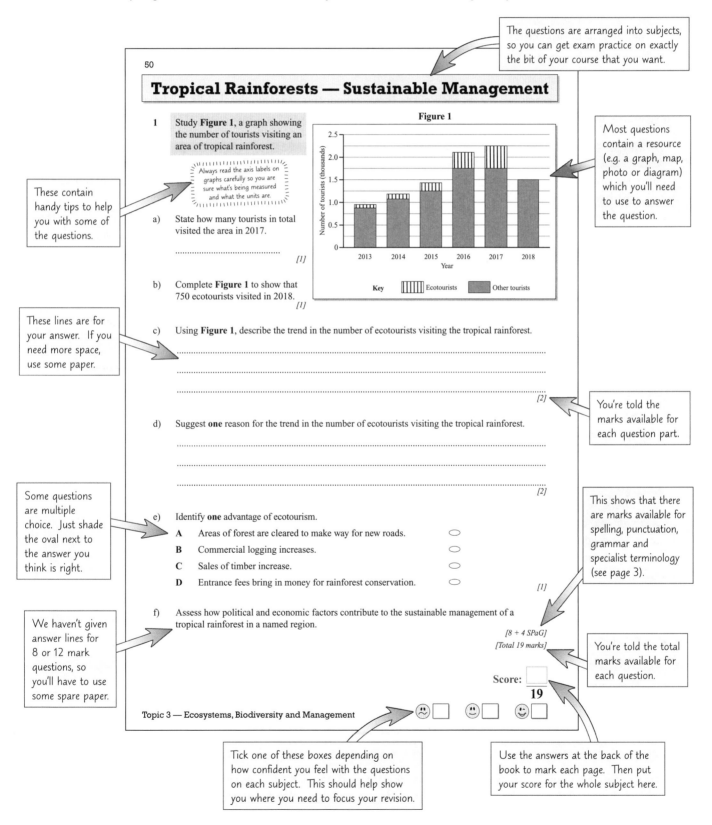

> Most questions contain a resource (e.g. a graph, map, photo or diagram) which you'll need to use to answer the question.

1 Study **Figure 1**, a graph showing the number of tourists visiting an area of tropical rainforest.

Always read the axis labels on graphs carefully so you are sure what's being measured and what the units are.

> These contain handy tips to help you with some of the questions.

Figure 1

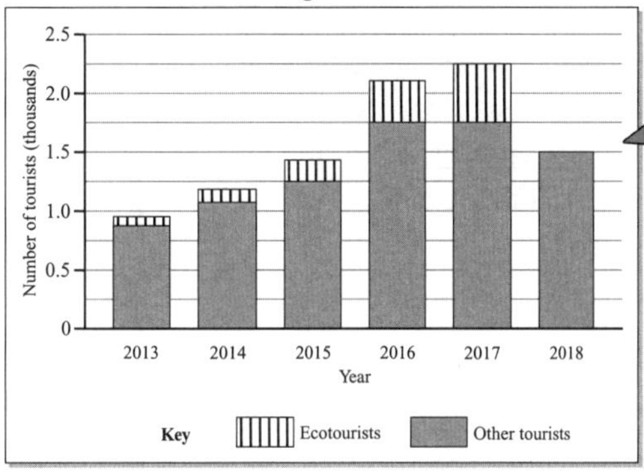

a) State how many tourists in total visited the area in 2017.

.... *[1]*

b) Complete **Figure 1** to show that 750 ecotourists visited in 2018. *[1]*

> These lines are for your answer. If you need more space, use some paper.

c) Using **Figure 1**, describe the trend in the number of ecotourists visiting the tropical rainforest.

....

....

.... *[2]*

> You're told the marks available for each question part.

d) Suggest **one** reason for the trend in the number of ecotourists visiting the tropical rainforest.

....

....

.... *[2]*

> Some questions are multiple choice. Just shade the oval next to the answer you think is right.

e) Identify **one** advantage of ecotourism.

A Areas of forest are cleared to make way for new roads. ⬭

B Commercial logging increases. ⬭

C Sales of timber increase. ⬭

D Entrance fees bring in money for rainforest conservation. ⬭

[1]

> This shows that there are marks available for spelling, punctuation, grammar and specialist terminology (see page 3).

f) Assess how political and economic factors contribute to the sustainable management of a tropical rainforest in a named region.

> We haven't given answer lines for 8 or 12 mark questions, so you'll have to use some spare paper.

[8 + 4 SPaG]

[Total 19 marks]

> You're told the total marks available for each question.

Score: ☐ / 19

Topic 3 — Ecosystems, Biodiversity and Management ☹ ☐ 😐 ☐ ☺ ☐

> Tick one of these boxes depending on how confident you feel with the questions on each subject. This should help show you where you need to focus your revision.

> Use the answers at the back of the book to mark each page. Then put your score for the whole subject here.

Exam Breakdown

Welcome to the wonderful world of <u>exam practice</u>. This book will help you get a bit of practice at the kind of questions they're going to throw at you in the exam. It'll also help you to figure out <u>what</u> you <u>need to revise</u> — try answering the questions for the topics you've learnt in class, and if there are any questions that you <u>can't answer</u> then <u>go back and revise that topic</u> some more.

You'll have to do Three Exams

GCSE Edexcel Geography A is divided into <u>three components</u>:

• The Physical Environment

• The Human Environment

• Geographical Investigations

You'll have to do <u>three exams</u> — <u>one</u> on each of the three <u>components</u>. <u>Geographical skills</u> will be assessed in <u>all</u> three exams, but <u>fieldwork</u> will only be assessed in <u>Paper 3</u>. All your <u>exams</u> will take place at the <u>end of the course</u>.

Paper 1: The Physical Environment

Paper 1 is divided into <u>three sections</u> (A, B and C). You <u>don't</u> have to answer questions on <u>all</u> of the topics in <u>Section A</u>.

<u>Section A: The Changing Landscapes of the UK</u>

• The Changing Landscapes of the UK plus

• TWO FROM Coastal Landscapes and Processes, River Landscapes and Processes OR Glaciated Upland Landscapes and Processes

<u>Section B: Weather Hazards and Climate Change</u>

<u>Section C: Ecosystems, Biodiversity and Management</u>

Here are the details for the <u>Paper 1 exam</u>:

	1 hour 30 minutes	94 marks in total	37.5% of your final mark

Paper 2: The Human Environment

Paper 2 is divided into <u>three sections</u> (A, B and C). You <u>don't</u> have to answer questions on <u>all</u> of the topics in <u>Section C</u>.

<u>Section A: Changing Cities</u>

<u>Section B: Global Development</u>

<u>Section C: Resource Management</u>

• Resource Management plus

• EITHER Energy Resource Management OR Water Resource Management

If you're not sure which of the optional themes you're studying, check with your teacher.

Here are the details for the <u>Paper 2 exam</u>:

	1 hour 30 minutes	94 marks in total	37.5% of your final mark

Paper 3: Geographical Investigations: Fieldwork and UK Challenges

Paper 3 is divided into <u>three sections</u> (A, B and C). For <u>Sections A</u> and <u>B</u> you need to answer questions about <u>fieldwork</u> in the environments you have chosen. Answer <u>all</u> the questions in <u>Section C</u>.

<u>Section A: Geographical Investigations — Physical Environments</u>

• EITHER River Landscapes OR Coastal Landscapes

<u>Section B: Geographical Investigations — Human Environments</u>

• EITHER Central/Inner Urban Areas OR Rural Settlements

<u>Section C: UK Challenges</u>

• These questions will be about <u>applying</u> what you have learnt for <u>Papers 1</u> and <u>2</u> to a <u>contemporary UK challenge</u>.

Here are the details for the <u>Paper 3 exam</u>:

	1 hour 30 minutes	64 marks in total	25% of your final mark

In <u>each exam</u>, there will be one question which has <u>4 extra marks</u> available for <u>spelling</u>, <u>punctuation</u> and <u>grammar</u> as well as the use of <u>specialist terminology</u>. These marks are <u>included</u> in the <u>total marks</u> given for each paper.

Answering Questions

Geography exams would be <u>lovely</u> if it wasn't for those <u>inconvenient questions</u>. A nice couple of hours of <u>peace and quiet</u> to just sit and let your mind wander... Unfortunately, daydreaming about your summer holiday don't <u>butter no parsnips</u>. So here's CGP's <u>top guide</u> to tackling those pesky questions.

Make Sure you Read the Question Properly

It's dead easy to <u>misread</u> the question and spend five minutes writing about the <u>wrong thing</u>.
Four simple tips can help you <u>avoid</u> this:

1) Figure out if it's a <u>case study question</u> — if the question wording includes 'using <u>named examples</u>' or 'for a <u>named country</u>' you need to include a case study or an example you've learnt about.

2) <u>Underline</u> the <u>command words</u> in the question (the ones that tell you <u>what to do</u>):

Command word	Means...
Identify, State or Name	Just give the <u>information</u> you're asked for. You <u>don't</u> need to give any reasons.
Calculate	Do some <u>maths</u> (yikes). Make sure you <u>show</u> your <u>working</u> to get full marks.
Describe	Write about what something is <u>like</u> or what the process <u>involves</u>. You <u>don't</u> need to give reasons but you should try to give as much <u>detail</u> as possible.
Explain	Write about <u>how</u> or <u>why</u> something happens (i.e. give <u>reasons</u>).
Compare	Write about the <u>similarities</u> AND <u>differences</u>.
Suggest	Write about <u>how</u> or <u>why</u> something might happen (i.e. give <u>reasons</u>), <u>applying</u> your <u>knowledge</u> to an unfamiliar situation.
Examine	Write about the different <u>processes</u> or <u>parts</u> of something, how they <u>fit</u> into the <u>bigger picture</u> and how they <u>interact</u> with each other.
Assess	<u>Weigh up</u> all the factors involved and decide how <u>significant</u> something (e.g. a statement or a cause) is.
Evaluate	Write about how <u>successful</u> something is, including both <u>pros</u> and <u>cons</u>. Make sure you come to a <u>conclusion</u>.
Discuss	Write about the <u>strengths</u> and <u>weaknesses</u> of <u>both</u> sides of an argument.

Answers to questions with 'explain' in them often include the word 'because' (or 'due to').

When writing about differences, 'whereas' is a good word to use in your answers.

3) <u>Underline</u> the <u>key words</u> (the ones that tell you what it's <u>about</u>), e.g. climate change, urbanisation, energy supply.

4) If the question says '<u>using Figure 2</u>', bloomin' well <u>make sure</u> you've talked about <u>what Figure 2 shows</u>. <u>Don't</u> just wheel out all of your <u>geographical knowledge</u> and forget all about the photo you're <u>supposed</u> to be <u>talking about</u>. <u>Re-read</u> the <u>question</u> and your <u>answer</u> when you've <u>finished</u>, just to check.

Some Questions are Level Marked

Questions worth <u>8 marks or more</u> with longer written answers are <u>level marked</u>, which means you need to do these <u>things</u> to get the <u>top level</u> and a <u>high mark</u>:

1) <u>Read</u> the question properly and figure out a <u>structure</u> for your answer before you start. Your answer needs to be well <u>organised</u> and <u>structured</u>, and written in a <u>logical</u> way.

2) If it's a <u>case study</u> question, include plenty of <u>relevant details</u>:
   - This includes things like <u>place names</u>, <u>dates</u>, <u>statistics</u>, names of <u>organisations</u> or <u>companies</u>.
   - Don't forget that they need to be <u>relevant</u> though — it's no good including the exact number of people killed in a drought when the question is about the <u>causes</u> of a drought.

3) Some questions have <u>4 extra marks</u> available for <u>spelling</u>, <u>punctuation</u> and <u>grammar</u>. To get <u>top marks</u> you need to:
   - Make sure your <u>spelling</u>, <u>punctuation</u> and <u>grammar</u> are <u>consistently correct</u>.
   - Write in a way that makes it <u>clear</u> what you mean.
   - Use a <u>wide range</u> of <u>geographical terms</u> (e.g. sustainable management) <u>correctly</u>.

Rocks and the UK Physical Landscape

1   Study **Figure 1**, which shows the distribution of different rock types in the UK.

a)   Which **two** of the following statements are true of metamorphic rocks?

Figure 1

    A   Metamorphic rocks are made when magma cools down and hardens.   ◯

    B   Sandstone is an example of a metamorphic rock.   ◯

    C   Metamorphic rocks are formed when other rocks are changed by heat and pressure.   ◯

    D   Metamorphic rocks are very soft and are easily weathered.   ◯

    E   Metamorphic rocks are harder and more compact than sedimentary rocks.   ◯

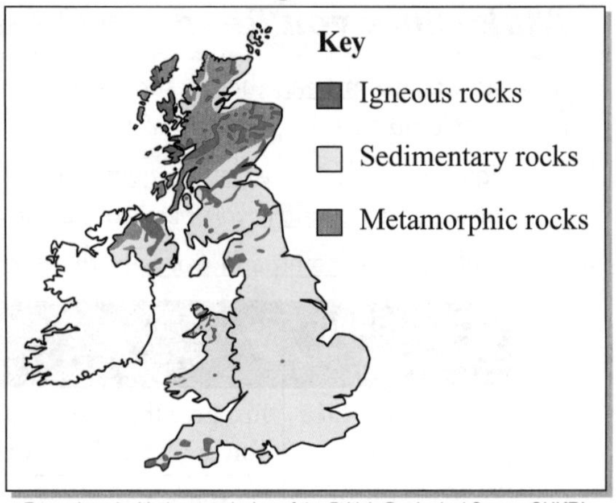

[2]

b)   i)   Give **one** example of a sedimentary rock.

Sand stone.

[1]

    ii)   Explain how sedimentary rocks are formed.

When sedimentary rock weathered layers of deposited material gets squashed together forming new rocks

[2]

c)   i)   Define the term 'igneous rock'.

Rocks formed when moltern lava cools down

[1]

    ii)   State **two** characteristics of igneous rock.

     1: ....

     2: ....

[2]

    iii)   Using **Figure 1**, describe the distribution of igneous rocks in the UK.

[2]

[Total 10 marks]

Rocks and the UK Physical Landscape

2   Study **Figure 2**, which shows an upland landscape made of granite in south west England.

Figure 2

a)   i)   State which type of rock granite is.

....
[1]

ii)   Suggest how the geology of the area resulted in the upland landscape shown in **Figure 2**.

....

....

....
[2]

b)   State **one** characteristic of the rock types which usually form lowlands in the UK.

....
[1]

c)   State **two** ways in which past glacial processes have shaped upland areas in the UK.

1:...

2:...
[2]

d)   Explain how past tectonic processes have shaped the UK landscape.

....

....

....

....

....
[4]
[Total 10 marks]

Score:

20

Topic 1 — The Changing Landscapes of the UK

Landscape Processes — Physical

1 Study **Figure 1**, a photo of an area in the Lake District, an upland area formed by glacial processes.

Figure 1

a) State **one** type of weathering that may be altering the landscape shown in **Figure 1**.

....
[1]

b) Suggest **two** ways that slope processes may be modifying the landscape shown in **Figure 1**.

1:...

....

2:...

....
[4]

c) Explain **one** way that climate may be influencing the physical processes in this landscape.

....

....

....
[2]
[Total 7 marks]

2 Study **Figure 2**, a photo of a lowland area in the UK.

Figure 2

Explain how the interaction of physical processes may lead to the formation of lowland landscapes such as the one shown in **Figure 2**.

....

....

....

....

....

....

....
[Total 3 marks]

Score:

10

Topic 1 — The Changing Landscapes of the UK

Landscape Processes — Human

1   Study **Figure 1**, an Ordnance Survey® map of Thetford,
     Norfolk, a lowland area in the east of England.

Figure 1

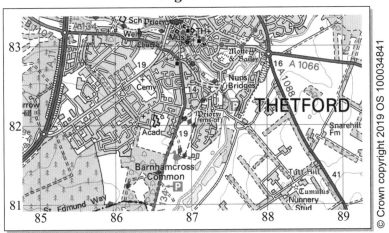

a)   Using **Figure 1**, identify **one** piece of evidence that agriculture is taking place in this area.

....

....
                                                                                                                                                          [1]

b)   Using **Figure 1**, identify **two** ways that human settlement has altered the landscape
      in grid square 8582.

      1:..

      2:..
                                                                                                                                                          [2]

c)   Using **Figure 1**, explain **one** way that forestry may be influencing the landscape.

      ....

      ....

      ....
                                                                                                                                                          [2]

d)   Identify **two** possible reasons why the land surrounding Thetford is suitable for arable farming.

      1:..

      2:..
                                                                                                                                                          [2]

e)   Explain how farming in upland areas is different from farming in lowland areas.

      ....

      ....

      ....
                                                                                                           [2]
                                                                                                    [Total 9 marks]   **Score:** ☐

 ☐   ☐   ☐

9

Topic 1 — The Changing Landscapes of the UK

Coastal Weathering and Erosion

1   Study **Figure 1**, which shows how the coastline of an area has changed over time.

Figure 1

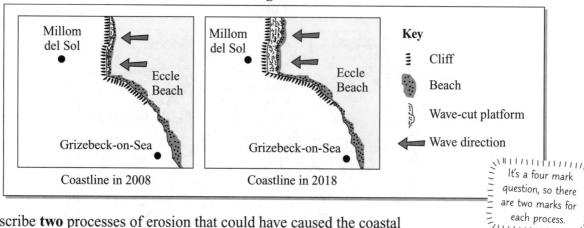

Coastline in 2008	Coastline in 2018	Key

It's a four mark question, so there are two marks for each process.

a)   Describe **two** processes of erosion that could have caused the coastal change shown in **Figure 1**.

1:...

....

....

2:...

....

....

[4]

b)   Explain how salt weathering could cause the cliffs shown in **Figure 1** to break up.

....

....

....

....

....

[4]

c)   Explain how a process of weathering, other than salt weathering, could affect the cliffs in **Figure 1**.

....

....

....

[2]

[Total 10 marks]

Score: ☐

10

 ☐   ☐   ☐

Coastal Transport and Deposition

1 Study **Figure 1**, a graph showing how the width of a beach varied along its length in the years 2010 and 2018.

Figure 1

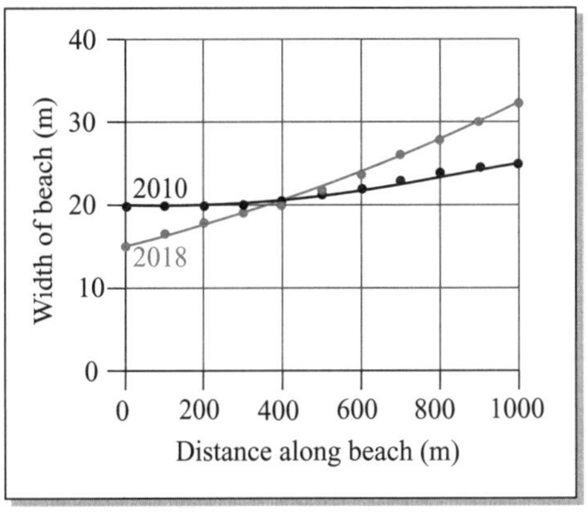

a) Using **Figure 1**, compare the width of the beach in 2010 with the width in 2018.

....

....

....

....

....

[3]

b) Explain how the changes in beach width shown in **Figure 1** occurred.

....

....

....

....

....

[4]

c) Name **two** processes by which material is transported on the seabed.

1:..

2:..

[2]

d) The total volume of material on the beach in **Figure 1** increased between 2010 and 2018 because large amounts of material, carried by sea water, were deposited on the coast.
Suggest **two** reasons for the high rate of deposition.

1:..

....

2:..

....

[2]

e) Name the type of wave that deposits material.

....

[1]

[Total 12 marks]

Score:

12

Coastal Landforms

1   Study **Figure 1**, a photograph showing coastal landforms in the UK.

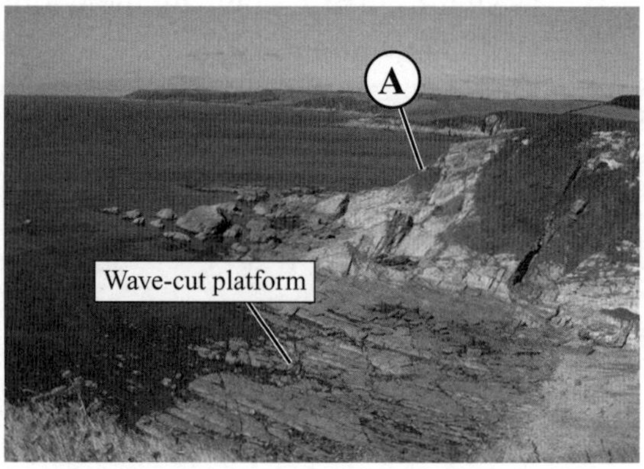

a)   Identify the type of landform labelled A in **Figure 1**.

   ....
   [1]

Figure 1

b)   Explain how the wave-cut platform in **Figure 1** was formed.

   ....

   ....

   ....

   ....

   ....
   [3]

c)   i)   Suggest how the changing average temperatures through the year might influence the rate of coastal retreat in **Figure 1**.

   ....

   ....

   ....
   [2]

   ii)   Explain **one** other way in which climate can influence the rate of cliff retreat in the UK.

   ....

   ....

   ....
   [2]

d)   For a named coastal landscape, explain how areas of concordant and/or discordant coastline have influenced the formation of the landscape.

   ....

   ....

   ....

   ....

   ....
   [4]

   [Total 12 marks]

Coastal Landforms

2   Study **Figure 2**, a photograph of a coastal area.

a)   Name the feature labelled A in **Figure 2** and explain how it was formed.

Figure 2

Feature:..
                                              [1]

....

....

....

....

....
                                                       [3]

b)   Label **Figure 2** to show an arch.
                                                       [1]

c)   Explain how the arch in **Figure 2** was formed.

....

....

....
                                                      [2]

[Total 7 marks]

3   Study **Figure 3**, a photograph of a coastal area.

Use evidence from **Figure 3** to suggest what this coastal area may look like in the future.

....

....

....

Figure 3

....

....

....

....

....

....

For this question you have to describe what the area will look like and explain why.

....
                                                      [Total 4 marks]

Coastal Landforms

4   Study **Figure 4**, an Ordnance Survey® map of a coastal area in Devon.

Figure 4

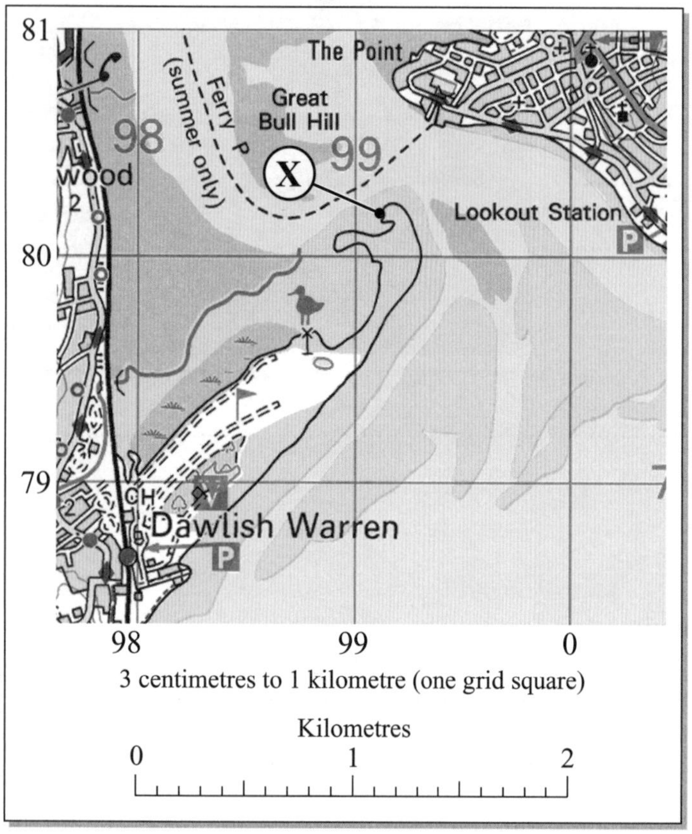

© Crown copyright 2019 OS 100034841

3 centimetres to 1 kilometre (one grid square)

Kilometres

a)   The end of the spit is marked X on **Figure 4**. Give the six figure grid reference for the end of the spit.

....
[1]

b)   Identify the distance between the end of the spit and Dawlish Warren station at 979786.

.... km
[1]

c)   Explain how the spit shown in **Figure 4** was formed.

....
....
....
....
....
[2]

d)   Suggest what could happen to the spit in **Figure 4** if it continued to grow.

....
....
....
[2]
[Total 6 marks]

5   Study **Figure 5**, a diagram showing a stretch of coastline.

Figure 5

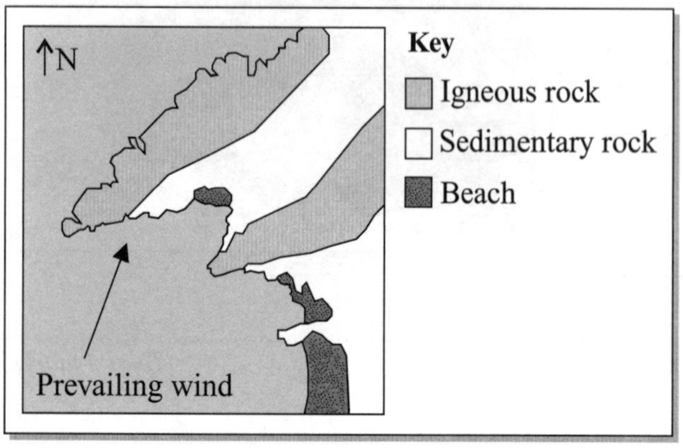

Key
☐ Igneous rock
☐ Sedimentary rock
☐ Beach

↑N

Prevailing wind

Examine how physical processes have interacted in the formation of the coastline shown in **Figure 5**.

[Total 8 marks]

Score:

37

Topic 1 — The Changing Landscapes of the UK

Human Activity at the Coast

1   In some parts of the UK, coastal areas are used for farming.

a)   Explain **one** way that using coastal land for agriculture can affect rates of cliff erosion.

....

....

....

[2]

b)   Explain how urbanisation can affect coastal landscapes.

....

....

....

[2]

[Total 4 marks]

2   **Figure 1** shows the frequencies of storms and floods over 10 years for a coastal area of the UK.

Figure 1

Year	2009	2010	2011	2012	2013	2014	2015	2016	2017	2018
Number of storms	0	1	3	3	4	3	5	5	6	7
Number of floods	0	0	1	2	3	2	4	4	5	5

a)   Calculate the mean number of floods per year.

....

[1]

b)   Suggest **one** threat to people from increased frequency of coastal flooding.

....

....

....

[2]

c)   Explain **one** way that human activities are causing change in a named coastal landscape.

....

....

....

[2]

[Total 5 marks]

Score:

9

Coastal Defences

1   Study **Figure 1**, a news article about coastal defences in Cliffall, a UK coastal town.

Figure 1

HOPE FOR CLIFFALL'S COASTLINE

Work is due to start next week on new defences for the Cliffall coastline. The town has been suffering from the effects of coastal erosion over the last few years but it's hoped the new defences will prevent further problems. The scheme will use a combination of defences, including groynes, rip-rap and beach nourishment. The work will be completed gradually over the next four years, with the groynes the top priority.

a)   Identify which of the coastal management strategies below is a soft engineering strategy.

     A   Beach nourishment   ⬭

     B   Sea wall   ⬭

     C   Groynes   ⬭

     D   Rip-rap   ⬭

[1]

b)   Explain how beach nourishment protects the coastline.

....

....

....

[2]

c)   State **two** disadvantages of using beach nourishment as a defence.

     1: ....

     2: ....

[2]

d)   Suggest why the coastal management strategy for Cliffall does not include managed retreat.

....

....

....

[2]

e)   Explain **one** way that hard engineering can lead to changes in coastal landscapes.

....

....

....

[2]

[Total 9 marks]

Score: ☐

9

River Processes

1   Study **Figure 1**, which shows the long profile of a river.

Figure 1

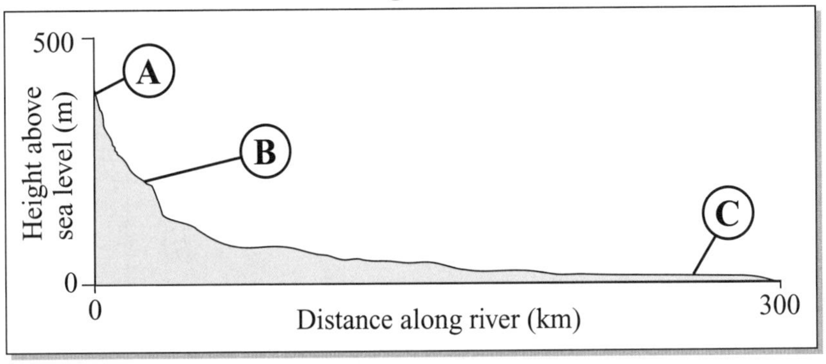

a)   Identify which part of the river is labelled A in **Figure 1**.

A   Mouth   ⬭

B   Source   ⬭

C   Lower course   ⬭

D   Meander   ⬭
[1]

b)   Identify which statement best describes how sediment size and shape change over a river's course.

A   Sediment becomes smaller and more well-rounded along a river's course.   ⬭

B   Sediment gets larger and more angular towards the mouth of a river.   ⬭

C   Sediment remains roughly the same size and shape along the course of a river.   ⬭

D   The size of sediment changes along the course of a river,
but sediment shape remains the same.   ⬭
[1]

c)   Explain how river discharge changes along the course of a river.

....

....

....
[2]

d)   Using a named example of a UK river, explain why the landscape of the upper course
is different from the lower course.

....

....

....

....

....
[4]

e)   Suggest how mechanical weathering could shape a river valley in the upper course.

....

....

....

....

....
[4]

[Total 12 marks]

River Processes

2   Study **Figure 2**, which shows how river velocity and particle size vary along the River Dance.

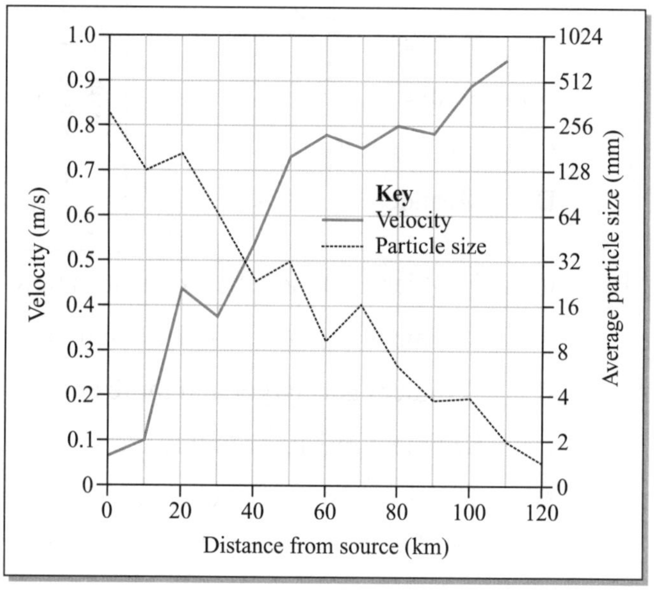

a)   Small gravel particles are transported by velocities above 0.1 m per second.
State the distance along the River Dance where the transportation of gravel starts.

....
[1]

Figure 2

b)   At 80 km along the River Dance, pebbles are being transported.
Give the velocity of the river at this point.

....
[1]

c)   Identify **one** process by which pebbles will be transported in the River Dance.

....
[1]

d)   Using **Figure 2**, suggest why deposition is the dominant process between 20 and 30 km.

....

....

....
[2]

e)   Explain why velocity increases along the river's course.

....

....

....
[2]

f)   Explain **one** process of erosion that is likely to be deepening the river channel in the upper course of the River Dance.

....

....

....
[2]

[Total 9 marks]

Score:

21

Topic 1 — The Changing Landscapes of the UK

River Landforms

1   Study **Figure 1**, which is an Ordnance Survey® map showing part of Snowdonia, Wales.

Figure 1

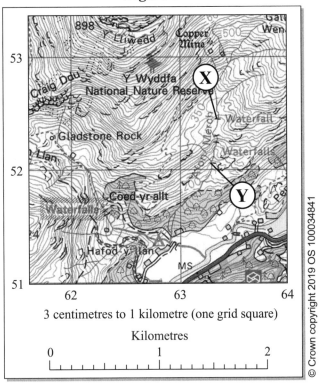

3 centimetres to 1 kilometre (one grid square)

Kilometres

© Crown copyright 2019 OS 100034841

a)   A waterfall is found at point X on **Figure 1**. State the six figure grid reference for the waterfall.

....

[1]

b)   Identify which waterfall, X or Y, is located on a steeper section of the river's course.

....

[1]

c)   Suggest why waterfalls have formed along this stretch of the Afon Merch.

....

....

....

[2]

d)   Explain how a gorge may form in the upper course of the Afon Merch.

....

....

....

....

[3]

[Total 7 marks]

Topic 1 — The Changing Landscapes of the UK

River Landforms

2   Study **Figure 2**, which shows the upper course of a river near Keswick, Cumbria.

a)   Identify **two** features in **Figure 2** which are characteristic of the upper course of a river basin.

Figure 2

1:...

2:...

[2]

b)   Suggest how the shape of the landscape in **Figure 2** has been influenced by the geology.

....

....

....

[2]

[Total 4 marks]

3   Study **Figure 3**, a cross profile of a river.

Figure 3

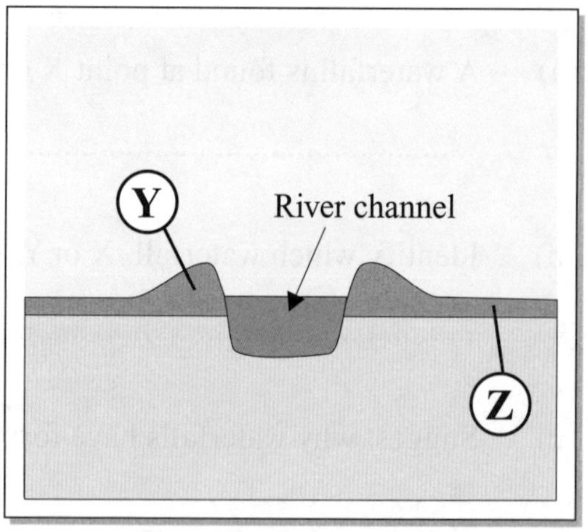

a)   i)   Identify the feature labelled Y on **Figure 3**.

   A   Levee   ◯

   B   Point bar   ◯

   C   Flood plain   ◯

   D   Gorge   ◯

[1]

ii)   Explain how the landform labelled Y in **Figure 3** is formed.

....

....

....

....

[3]

b)   Explain how the landform labelled Z in **Figure 3** builds up over time.

....

....

....

[2]

[Total 6 marks]

River Landforms

4   Study **Figure 4**, a labelled photograph of a meander.

Figure 4

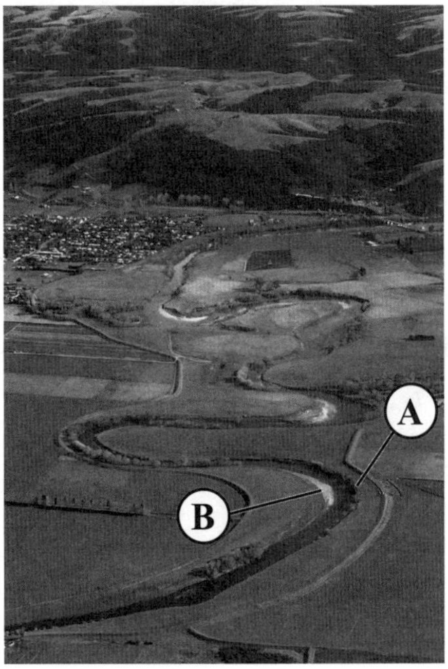

a)   i)   Name a feature likely to be found at the part of the river labelled A in **Figure 4** and explain its formation.

....

....

....

....

....

....

....

[3]

ii)   State **two** types of erosion that are likely to be involved in the formation of this feature.

1: ....

2: ....

[2]

b)   Name a feature likely to be found at the part of the river labelled B in **Figure 4** and explain its formation.

....

....

....

....

[3]

c)   Explain how an ox-bow lake could form on the river shown in **Figure 4**.

....

....

....

....

....

[4]

[Total 12 marks]

Score: ☐

29

Topic 1 — The Changing Landscapes of the UK

Climate, Weather and River Landscapes

1   Storms and droughts affect river landscapes and processes.

a)   Explain **one** way that a storm could affect landforms in the lower course of a river.

....

....

....

[2]

b)   Explain **one** way that droughts can affect river processes.

....

....

....

[2]

[Total 4 marks]

2   Study **Figure 1**, a photo of an upland river landscape in Scotland, which has a cool, wet climate.

a)   Explain **one** way that the climate might have affected rates of chemical weathering in the landscape shown in **Figure 1**.

Figure 1

....

....

....

....

....

....
[2]

b)   Explain **two** other ways that the climate could have affected the landscape in **Figure 1**.

1:..

....

....

2:..

....

....

[4]

[Total 6 marks]

Score: ☐

10

Topic 1 — The Changing Landscapes of the UK

River Flooding

1   Study **Figure 1**, a map of the River Eden basin in the north west of England.

a)   i)   The city of Carlisle is vulnerable
to flooding. Explain how human
factors can increase the risk of
flooding in urban areas.

Figure 1

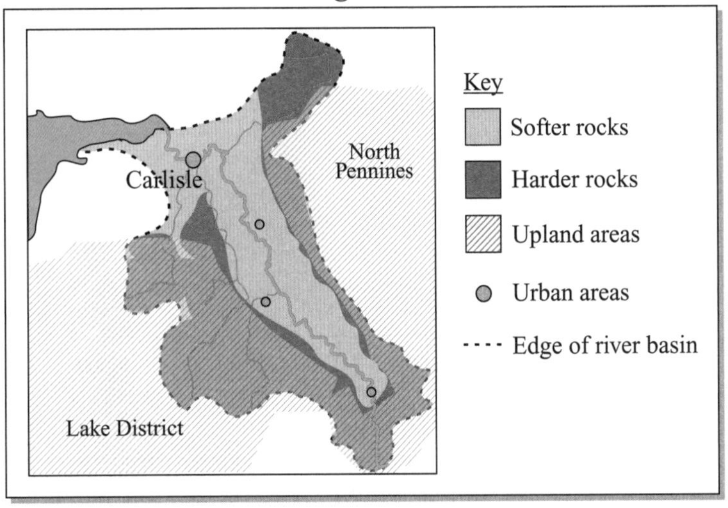

Key
Softer rocks
Harder rocks
Upland areas
Urban areas
Edge of river basin

North
Pennines

Carlisle

Lake District

....

....

....

....

....

....

....

....

[3]

ii)   Using evidence from **Figure 1**, suggest **one** physical factor
which could increase the risk of flooding in Carlisle.

....

....

....

[2]

b)   Explain how prolonged rainfall before a storm event
can lead to a more rapid increase in river discharge.

....

....

....

....

[3]

c)   Explain how geology can affect the risk of flooding.

....

....

....

[2]

[Total 10 marks]

Topic 1 — The Changing Landscapes of the UK

River Flooding

2   Study **Figure 2**, which shows storm hydrographs for two rivers.

Figure 2

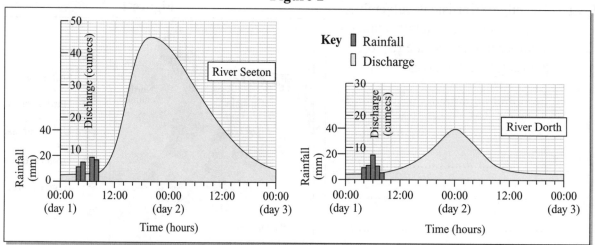

a)   i)   State the time at which the River Seeton was at peak discharge.

....
[1]

ii)   Complete the hydrograph for the River Seeton to show that the area
received 35 mm of rainfall at 06:00 on day 1.

[1]

iii)   Peak rainfall around the River Dorth was at 06:00 on day 1.   State the lag time.

....
[1]

b)   Identify which river is more likely to flood.   Give a reason for your answer.

....

....

....
[2]

c)   State **two** impacts that flooding can have on people.

1:..

2:..
[2]

d)   Explain **one** way that flooding can affect the environment.

....

....

....
[2]

[Total 9 marks]

Score:

19

Topic 1 — The Changing Landscapes of the UK

Human Activities in River Landscapes

1   Study **Figure 1**, which shows some of the engineering
     strategies used to combat flooding along the River Joiner.

Figure 1

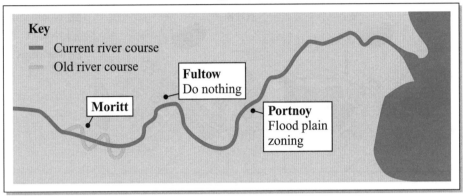

a)   i)   Identify the engineering strategy that has been used to protect Moritt.

     ....
     [1]

     ii) Explain how the engineering strategy at Moritt could cause problems in Fultow.

     ....

     ....

     ....
     [2]

     iii) Explain the benefits of the engineering strategy being used at Portnoy.

     ....

     ....

     ....
     [2]

b)   Explain how washlands can be used as a flood defence.

     ....

     ....

     ....
     [2]

c)   Explain **one** way in which building a dam and reservoir
     could change the landscape elsewhere along the river.

     ....

     ....

     ....
     [2]

[Total 9 marks]

Topic 1 — The Changing Landscapes of the UK

Human Activities in River Landscapes

2   Study **Figure 2**, which shows changes in land use around the River Run over the last 50 years.

Figure 2

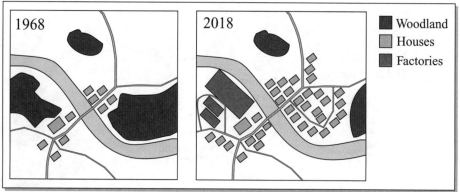

a)   Identify **one** way in which land use has changed around the River Run.

....

....
[1]

b)   Explain **two** ways in which the changes in land use shown in **Figure 2**
could affect river processes.

1:...

....

....

2:...

....

....
[4]

c)   Explain **one** way in which agriculture can affect river processes.

....

....

....
[2]

d)   Examine the impacts of human activities on a named river landscape in the UK.

[8]

[Total 15 marks]

Score: [ ]

24

Topic 1 — The Changing Landscapes of the UK

 [ ]   [ ]   [ ]

Glacial Erosion and Landforms

1   Study **Figure 1**, an Ordnance Survey® map of part of the Lake District.

a)   Identify the landform at 352150.

     A   Glacial trough   ○

     B   Arête   ○

     C   Roche moutonnée   ○

     D   Hanging valley   ○

[1]

Figure 1

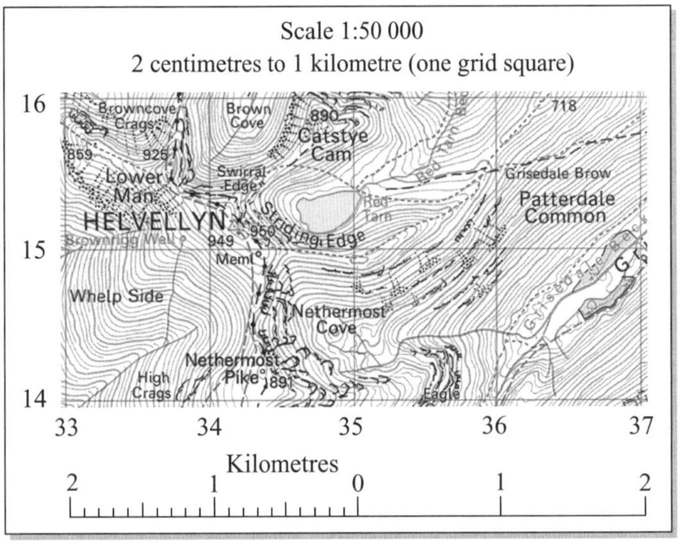

b)   i)   Give the **four** figure grid reference of a grid square that contains a glacial trough.

     ....
[1]

   ii) Explain how glacial troughs are formed.

     ....

     ....

     ....
[2]

c)   Using **Figure 1**, state how far it is between the summits of Catstye Cam and Nethermost Pike.

.... km
[1]

d)   **Figure 2** is a photo of the area shown in the map in **Figure 1**.

   i)   Identify the type of glacial landform labelled A in **Figure 2**.

     ....
[1]

   ii) Explain how the landform labelled A is formed.

Figure 2

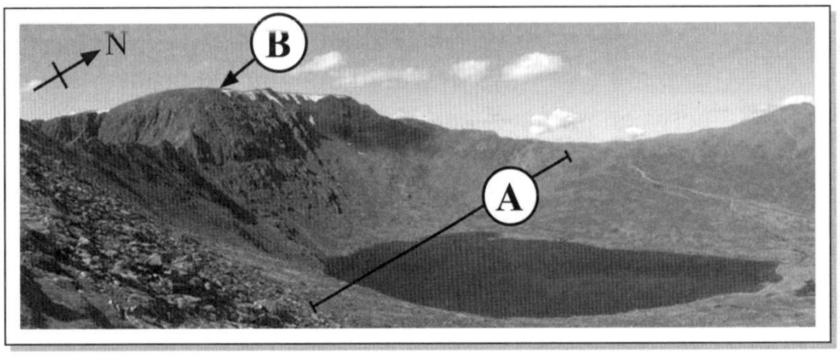

     ....

     ....

     ....

     ....
[3]

e)   The photograph in **Figure 2** was taken from 350150.
Using **Figure 1** and **Figure 2**, name the summit labelled B.

....

[1]

[Total 10 marks]

Glacial Erosion and Landforms

2 Study **Figure 3** and **Figure 4**, photographs of landforms in glaciated upland landscapes.

Figure 3

Figure 4

a) i) Identify the glacial landform labelled W in **Figure 3**.

    A   Truncated spur   ◯

    B   Roche moutonnée   ◯

    C   Tarn   ◯

    D   Hanging valley   ◯

Always double check you're talking about the right feature in a labelled photograph.

[1]

ii) Explain how this landform is formed.

....

....

....

....

[3]

b) Explain **two** ways in which moving ice eroded the landscape to create the change in gradient between points X and Y in **Figure 4**.

1:..

....

2:..

....

[4]

c) Explain how an arête is formed.

....

....

....

[2]

[Total 10 marks]

Score: ☐

20

 ☐   ☐   ☺ ☐

Glacial Landforms and Processes

1 Study **Figure 1**, a photograph of truncated spurs in Scotland.

Figure 1

a) Explain how truncated spurs form.

....

....

....

....

....
[2]

b) Describe how mass movement might occur on the truncated spurs in **Figure 1**.

....

....

....
[2]

[Total 4 marks]

2 Study **Figure 2**, which shows average temperature data for a glaciated area in the UK.

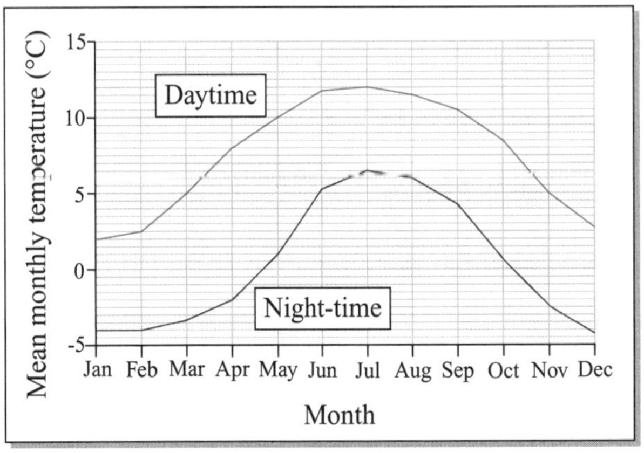

a) i) Calculate the range in daytime temperature through the year.

Figure 2

.... °C
[1]

ii) Calculate the difference between the mean daytime and night-time temperatures for February.

.... °C
[1]

b) Using **Figure 2**, explain **one** way in which variations in temperature can affect physical processes in glaciated upland landscapes.

Daytime

Night-time

Mean monthly temperature (°C)

Jan Feb Mar Apr May Jun Jul Aug Sep Oct Nov Dec

Month

....

....

....

....

....
[4]

[Total 6 marks]

Score:

10

Topic 1 — The Changing Landscapes of the UK

Glacial Transportation and Deposition

1 Study **Figure 1**, a diagram showing depositional landforms on the path of a former glacier.

a) Identify the depositional feature labelled X on **Figure 1**.

Figure 1

A   Terminal moraine   ◯

B   Roche moutonnée   ◯

C   Ground moraine   ◯

D   Drumlin   ◯

[1]

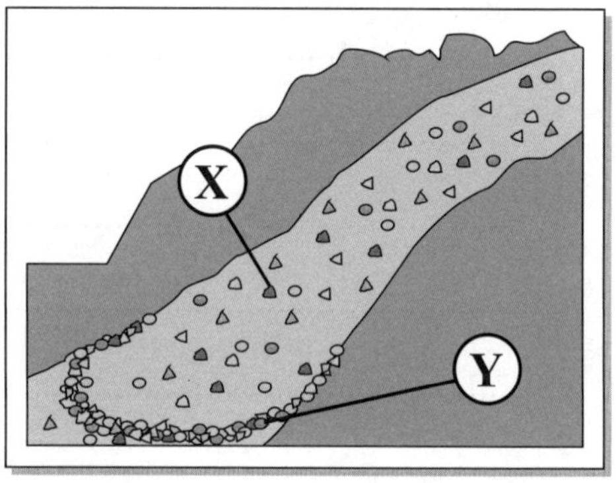

b) Give **one** way in which glaciers transport material.

....

....

....

[1]

c) Explain the formation of the feature labelled Y on **Figure 1**.

....

....

....

....

[3]

[Total 5 marks]

2 Study **Figure 2**, a sketch map of a crag and tail.

Figure 2

a) Label the sketch map to show the direction of ice flow.

[1]

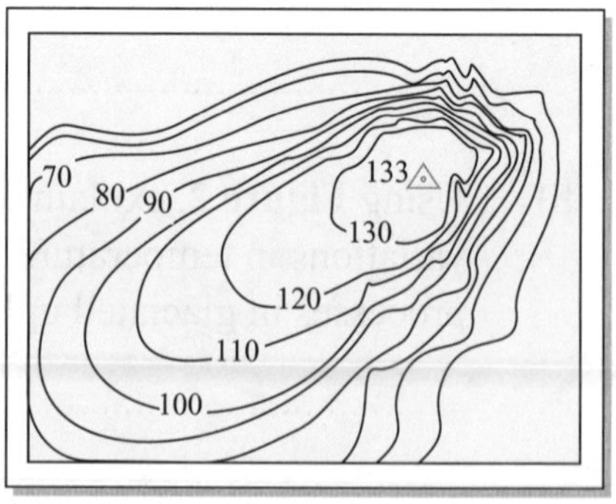

b) Explain how a crag and tail are formed.

....

....

....

....

....

....

[4]

[Total 5 marks]

Score:

10

Human Activities in Glaciated Landscapes

1   Study **Figure 1**, a photograph showing land use in a glaciated upland landscape in Scotland.

Figure 1

a)   State **two** land uses shown in **Figure 1**.

1:..

2:..
                                                                                                        [2]

b)   Explain **one** way in which building settlements can affect physical processes in glaciated uplands.

....

....

....
                                                                                                        [2]

c)   Compare the impacts of farming livestock and planting trees for forestry on physical processes
      in glaciated upland landscapes.

....

....

....

....
                                                                                                        [3]

d)   State **one** advantage and **one** disadvantage of water storage and supply developments
      in glaciated upland landscapes.

Advantage:...

....

Disadvantage:..

....
                                                                                                        [2]
                                                                                             [Total 9 marks]

Human Activities in Glaciated Landscapes

2   Study **Figure 2**, a graph showing information on the replanting of native woodland
    and spending by tourists and for a UK National Park in a glaciated landscape.

a)   Using **Figure 2**, state the lowest amount
     of native woodland replanted in the
     National Park in any **one** year

     ....
                                                    [1]

Figure 2

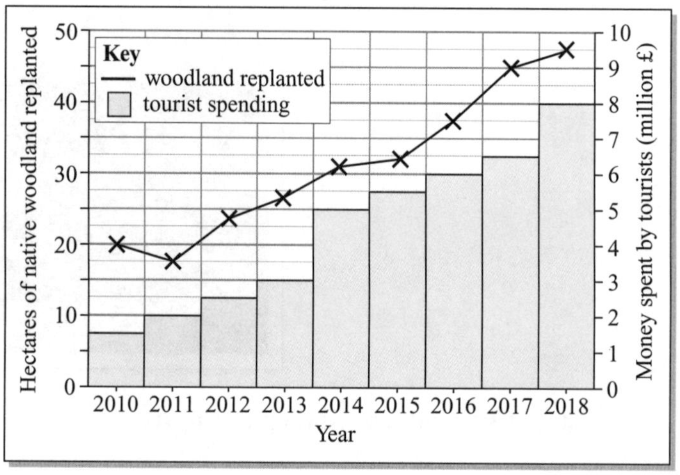

b)   Suggest why glaciated upland landscapes
     are often popular with tourists.

     ....

     ....

     ....

     ....
                                                                                                                        [2]

c)   State **one** way in which recreation and tourism can change the landscape in glaciated uplands.

     ....

     ....
                                                                                                                        [1]

d)   Using **Figure 2**, suggest **one** advantage of tourism for the National Park.

     ....

     ....

     ....
                                                                                                                        [2]

e)   State **two** disadvantages of renewable energy generation in glaciated upland landscapes.

     1:..

     ....

     2:..

     ....
                                                                                                                        [2]

f)   For a named glaciated upland landscape in the UK, examine how human activities
     have affected physical processes.
                                                                                                                        [8]

                                                                                                          [Total 16 marks]

                                                                                          Score: ☐
                                                                                          ‾‾‾‾‾‾‾
                                                                                          25

Global Atmospheric Circulation & Heat Transfer

1   Study **Figure 1**, a map of the world showing bands of high and low pressure and surface winds.

Figure 1

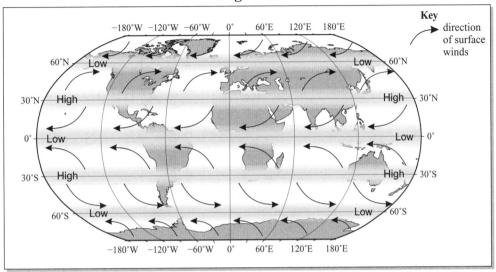

a)   Which of the following descriptions matches the normal weather conditions at a high pressure belt?

A   Low rainfall, often cloudy.   ◯

B   High rainfall, often cloudy.   ◯

C   Low rainfall, rarely cloudy.   ◯

D   High rainfall, rarely cloudy.   ◯

[1]

b)   Identify the latitude which receives the most solar radiation.

....
[1]

c)   Heat energy is distributed around the Earth by global atmospheric circulation and ocean currents.

i)   Explain how atmospheric circulation distributes heat energy from the equator to the poles.

....

....

....

....
[3]

ii) Explain how ocean currents are created by changes to water density at the poles.

....

....

....
[2]

[Total 7 marks]

Score: ☐

7

Natural Climate Change

1 Study **Figure 1**, a graph showing temperature changes during the Quaternary period.

a) Describe the general patterns shown in **Figure 1**.

Figure 1

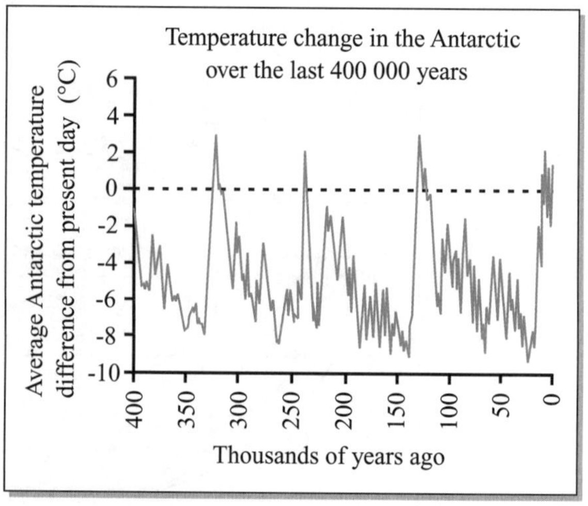
Temperature change in the Antarctic over the last 400 000 years
Average Antarctic temperature difference from present day (°C)
6
4
2
0
-2
-4
-6
-8
-10
400
350
300
250
200
150
100
50
0
Thousands of years ago

....

....

....

....

....

....

.... *[2]*

b) The temperature changes shown in **Figure 1** were worked out from ice core records. Explain how ice cores can be used to provide evidence of climate change during the Quaternary period.

....

....

.... *[2]*

c) Explain **two** possible causes of the changes in temperature between 400 000 and 100 000 years ago shown in **Figure 1**.

1:...

....

....

2:...

....

.... *[4]*

d) Suggest **one** source of evidence, other than ice cores, that scientists may have used to work out how the climate has changed over the last 1000 years.

....

....

.... *[2]*

[Total 10 marks]

Score: ____ / **10**

Climate Change — Human Activity

1   Study **Figure 1**, a photograph of a coal-fired power plant in South Africa.

a)   Explain how burning coal can lead to an increase in global temperatures.

Figure 1

....

....

....

....

....

....
[3]

b)   Explain how **one** other human activity may contribute to climate change.

....

....

....
[2]

[Total 5 marks]

2   Study **Figure 2**, which shows the maize yield and annual rainfall for a low latitude farm in Central Africa.

Figure 2

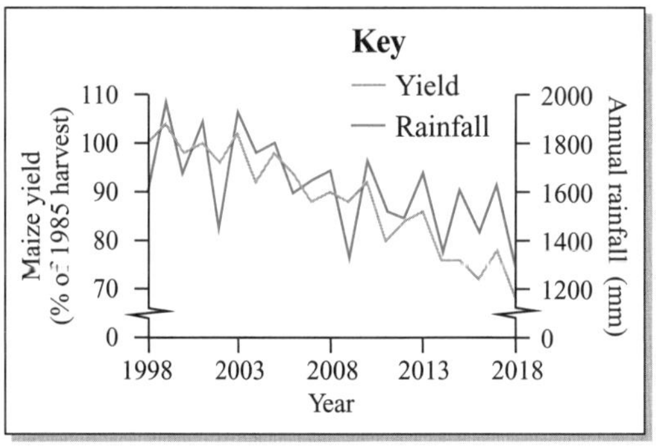

a)   i)   Using **Figure 2**, describe how climate change may be affecting crop yields in low latitude areas.

....

....

....

....
[2]

ii)   State **one** possible effect on people of the trends in crop yield shown in **Figure 4**.

....

....
[1]

b)   Identify **one** negative effect that climate change may have on the environment.

....

....
[1]

[Total 4 marks]

Score: ☐

9

 ☐   ☐   ☐

Topic 2 — Weather Hazards and Climate Change

UK Climate

1   Study **Figure 1**, which shows mean maximum temperatures in **two** different locations in the UK.

a)   State the mean maximum August temperature for Location A.

....
[1]

Figure 1

b)   Complete the graph to show that Location C has a mean maximum December temperature of 7 °C.

[1]

c)   Explain which location is likely to be at the highest altitude.

....

....
[2]

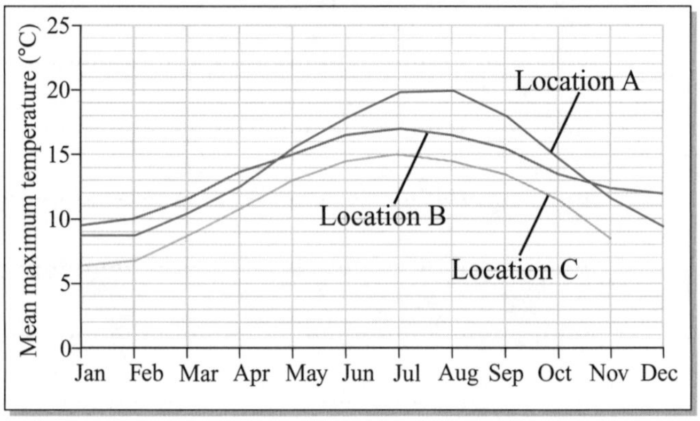

d)   State **one** example of how the climate of the UK has changed in the last 1000 years.

....

....
[1]
[Total 5 marks]

2   Study **Figure 2**, which shows average annual rainfall in the UK.

Figure 2

a)   i)   Identify which of the following statements is correct.

   A   The south of the UK receives little rain.   ◯

   B   Rainfall is higher in Cardiff than in London.   ◯

   C   Rainfall is higher in the east of the UK than in the west.   ◯

   D   Scotland generally has low rainfall.   ◯
[1]

   ii)   Explain **one** reason for the distribution of rainfall shown in **Figure 2**.

   ....

   ....

   ....
[2]

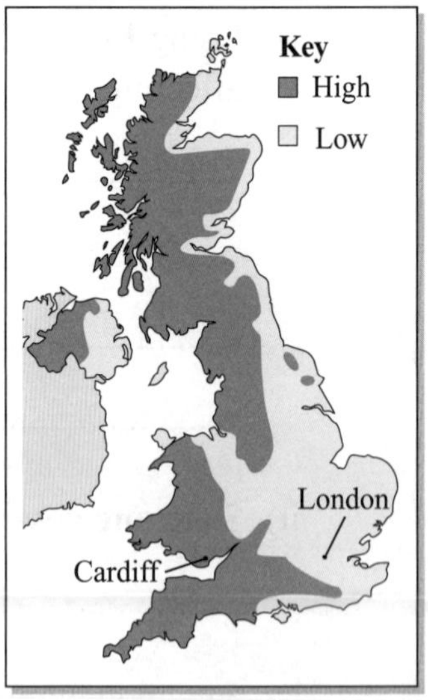

b)   Suggest why the UK has warmer winter temperatures than countries at similar latitudes in continental Europe.

....

....

....
[2]
[Total 5 marks]

Score: ☐
10

⌣☐   ☺☐   ☺☐

Tropical Cyclones

1   Study **Figure 1**, a map showing the
     areas affected by tropical cyclones.

Figure 1

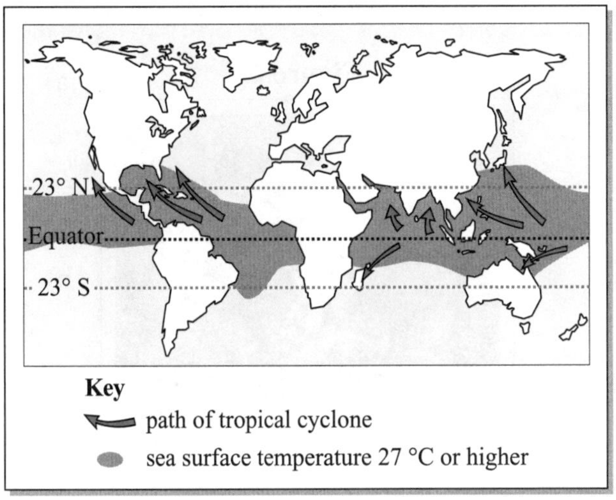

Key
↙ path of tropical cyclone
● sea surface temperature 27 °C or higher

a)   Using **Figure 1**, describe the global distribution
     of tropical cyclones.

     ....

     ....

     ....

     ....

     ....
     [2]

b)   Explain the seasonal distribution of tropical cyclones in the northern hemisphere.

     ....

     ....

     ....
     [2]

c)   Explain how tropical cyclones form.

     ....

     ....

     ....

     ....

     ....
     [4]

d)   State **two** features of tropical cyclones.

     1:...

     2:...
     [2]

e)   Identify which statement best describes how the frequency
     and distribution of tropical storms change over time.

     A   The distribution stays the same, but the frequency varies from year to year.   ⬭

     B   The distribution varies, but the frequency stays roughly the same each year.   ⬭

     C   The distribution stays the same, but the frequency decreases each year.   ⬭

     D   The distribution and the frequency stay exactly the same each year.   ⬭
     [1]

     [Total 11 marks]

Tropical Cyclones

2   Study **Figure 2**, a map showing the track of Hurricane Sandy in 2012. Hurricane Sandy had a Category 3 rating on the Saffir-Simpson scale when it made landfall in Cuba.

Figure 2

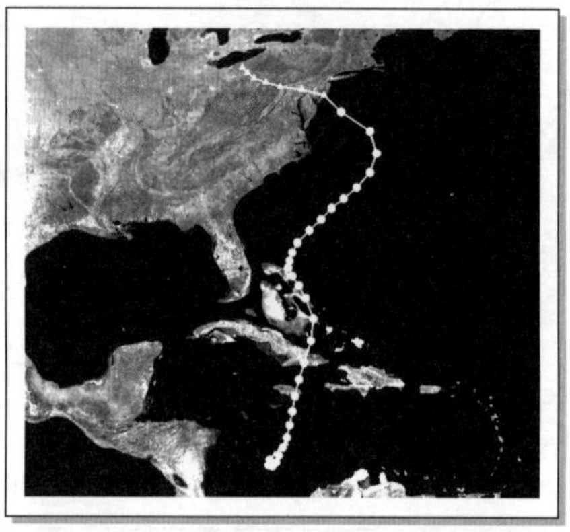

a)   State the main physical characteristic of the hurricane that is measured to give its category rating.

....
[1]

b)   Hurricane Sandy's wind speeds decreased as it moved away from the equator. Suggest **one** reason for this.

....

....
[1]

c)   State **two** natural hazards, other than high wind speeds, that tropical cyclones can cause.

1:..

2:..
[2]
[Total 4 marks]

3   Study **Figure 3**, a photograph of a city affected by a tropical cyclone.

a)   Using **Figure 3**, identify **two** possible social impacts of tropical cyclones.

Figure 3

1:...

....

2:...

....
[2]

b)   Explain **two** environmental impacts of a tropical cyclone in a named emerging or developing country.

1:..

....

....

2:..

....

....
[4]
[Total 6 marks]

Tropical Cyclones

4   Study **Figure 4**, which shows some information about two tropical cyclones.

Figure 4

	Tropical Cyclone A	Tropical Cyclone B
Location	Developed country	Emerging country
Category (Saffir-Simpson)	5	2
Estimated cost of damage	US$6 billion	US$2 billion
Buildings destroyed	3540	7836

a)   i)   Calculate the ratio of the cost of the damage caused by Tropical Cyclone A
           to the cost of the damage caused by Tropical Cyclone B.

           ....
                                                                                                                              [1]

      ii) Suggest **one** reason why more buildings were destroyed by Tropical Cyclone B.

           ....

           ....

           ....
                                                                                                                              [2]

b)   Explain how a country's level of development affects the economic impacts of tropical cyclones.

      ....

      ....

      ....

      ....
                                                                                                                              [3]

c)   Describe how organisations responded to a tropical cyclone in a named developed country.

      ....

      ....

      ....
                                                                                                                              [2]

d)   Referring to **two** countries with contrasting levels of development, assess the
      differences in how individuals and governments respond to tropical cyclones.
                                                                                                                              [8]
                                                                                                              [Total 16 marks]

Score:

Drought

1 Study **Figure 1**, which shows average climate data for a town in an arid country, and **Figure 2**, which shows the weather recorded for the same town in 2018, when there was a drought.

Figure 1

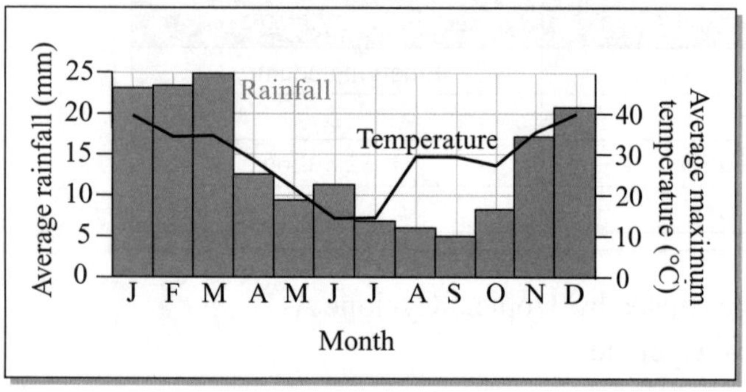

Figure 2

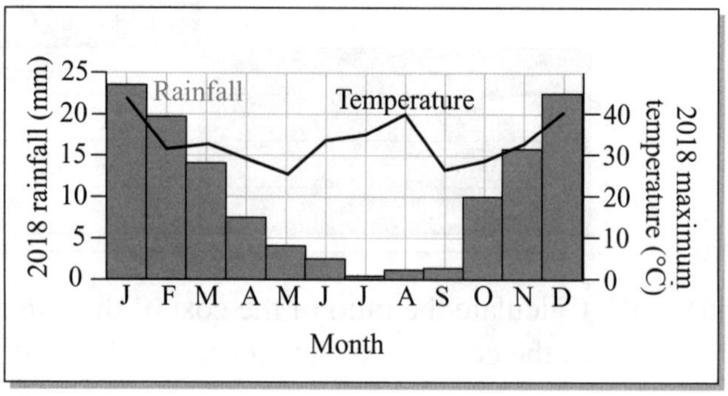

a) i) State the average rainfall for March.

.... mm

[1]

ii) Using **Figure 1**, explain why this location is an arid environment.

....

....

....

[2]

b) Using **Figure 1** and **Figure 2**, explain **two** reasons why there was a drought in 2018.

1:...

....

....

2:...

....

....

[4]

c) Explain **two** ways that droughts can be hazardous to people and ecosystems.

1:...

....

....

2:...

....

....

[4]

[Total 11 marks]

Topic 2 — Weather Hazards and Climate Change

Drought

2 Study **Figure 3**, which shows how the severity of droughts varies across the world.

a) Describe the global distribution of areas affected by droughts of medium to high severity.

Figure 3

> Refer to named regions or countries in your answer.

23° N
Equator
23° S

Key ☐ Low to medium severity ☐ Medium severity ☐ Medium to high severity

....

....

....

....

....

....

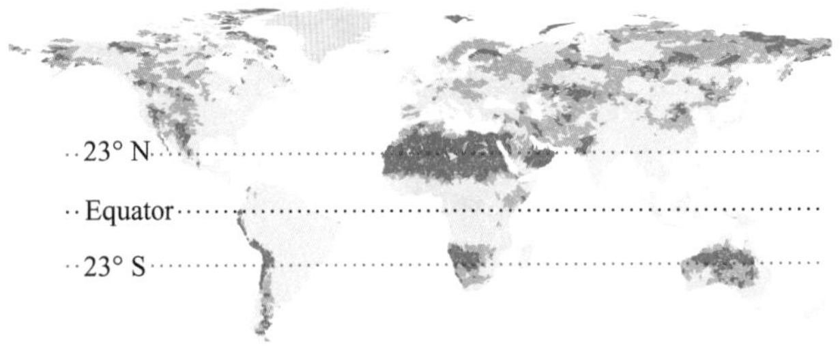

[3]

b) Explain the effect of global atmospheric circulation on the distribution of droughts shown in **Figure 3**.

....

....

....

....

[3]

[Total 6 marks]

3 Responses to drought can vary depending on a country's level of development.

a) State **two** ways that governments in a named developed country responded to a drought.

1:...

....

2:...

....

[2]

b) Assess the following statement, referring to **two** named examples in your answer.
"The impacts of drought are less severe in developed countries than in developing or emerging countries."

[8 + 4 SPaG]

[Total 14 marks]

Score: ☐

31

 ☐   ☐   ☐

Topic 2 — Weather Hazards and Climate Change

Topic 3 — Ecosystems, Biodiversity and Management

Global Ecosystems

1   Study **Figure 1**, a map showing the distribution of some of the world's large-scale ecosystems.

Figure 1

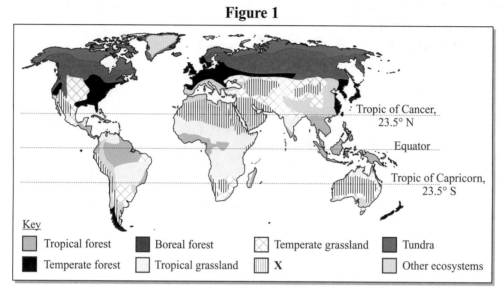

a)   Identify the large-scale ecosystem labelled 'X' in **Figure 1**.

....
[1]

b)   Using **Figure 1**, describe the global distribution of tropical forests.

....

....

....
[2]

c)   Describe the climate in tundra environments.

....

....

....
[2]

d)   Using examples from **Figure 1**, explain how climate affects the distribution of large-scale ecosystems.

....

....

....

....
[3]

[Total 8 marks]

Global Ecosystems

2 Study **Figure 2**, which shows temperature and rainfall data for an area of forest.

a) Which month has the highest average temperature?

....
                   [1]

b) Identify the type of forest ecosystem that is likely to have developed in the climate shown in **Figure 2**.

....
                   [1]

c) Describe the vegetation found in this type of forest.

....

....

....

....

....
                   [2]

[Total 4 marks]

Figure 2

Month	Average temperature / °C	Average rainfall / mm
January	2	64
February	5	42
March	6	33
April	12	42
May	19	45
June	19	48
July	21	69
August	19	62
September	12	45
October	10	55
November	4	65
December	2	52

3 Study **Figure 3**, a photograph of tropical grassland.

a) Identify which of the following is **not** a characteristic of the climate of tropical grasslands.

  A Long sunshine hours through the year ◯

  B Distinct wet and dry seasons ◯

  C High rainfall (over 1500 mm/yr) ◯

  D Hot summers (up to 40 °C) ◯
                [1]

Figure 3

b) Using **Figure 3** and your own knowledge, describe the vegetation of tropical grasslands.

....

....

....

....
                                    [2]

[Total 4 marks]

Global Ecosystems

4 Boreal forests are home to species such as the snowshoe hare.

a) Name **one** other animal found in boreal forests.

....
[1]

b) State where boreal forests are found.

....
[1]

c) Suggest why boreal forests might be more suited to areas of high altitude than other ecosystems.

....

....

....
[2]
[Total 3 marks]

5 Study **Figure 4**, which shows soil profiles for a desert and a temperate grassland.

a) Suggest how the soils in a tropical grassland would be different from those in a temperate grassland.

....

....

....

....

....
[2]

Figure 4

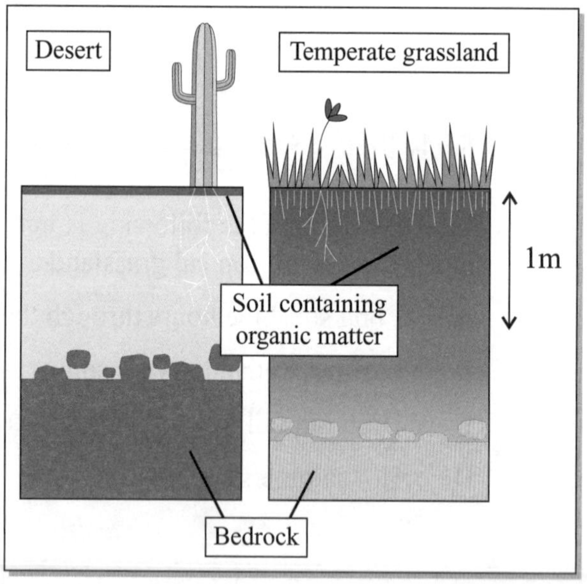

Desert | Temperate grassland

1m

Soil containing organic matter

Bedrock

b) With reference to **Figure 4**, explain how soil type affects the distribution of large-scale ecosystems.

....

....

....

....

....

....
[3]
[Total 5 marks]

Score:

24

Topic 3 — Ecosystems, Biodiversity and Management

Humans and the Biosphere

1   The biosphere provides humans with lots of resources.

a)   Explain how the biosphere can provide people with medicines.

....

....

[1]

b)   Explain **one** reason why the exploitation of the biosphere for mineral resources is increasing.

....

....

....

[2]

[Total 3 marks]

2   Study **Figure 1**, a table showing forest cover in Terra Spoglio between 1970 and 2010.

Figure 1

Year	Area of forest cover remaining (million ha)
1970	5.42
1980	5.40
1990	4.89
2000	4.61
2010	4.04

a)   Using **Figure 1**, calculate the percentage change in forest cover between 1970 and 2010.

....

[1]

b)   The total area of Terra Spoglio is 19 million hectares.
Calculate the percentage of Terra Spoglio that was covered by forest in 1990.

....

[1]

c)   Explain why increasing demand for energy is causing deforestation of the biosphere.

....

....

....

[2]

[Total 4 marks]

Score: [ ]

7

Topic 3 — Ecosystems, Biodiversity and Management

UK Ecosystems

1   Study **Figure 1**, which shows the distribution of the UK's main terrestrial ecosystems.

a)   State **one** example of an ecosystem that is only found in upland areas.

Figure 1

....

[1]

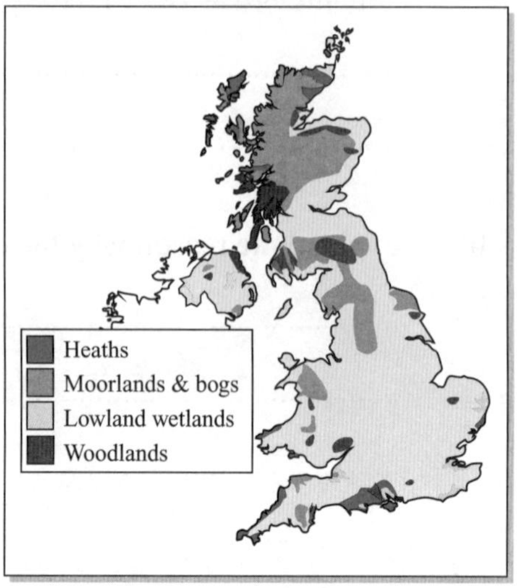

b)   Which of these statements is **not** correct?

    A   Wetlands are found around rivers and lakes.   ◯

    B   Woodlands cover most of the UK.   ◯

    C   Heaths are often found near coasts.   ◯

    D   Moorlands are mostly found in Scotland and the north of England.   ◯

[1]

| Heaths |
| Moorlands & bogs |
| Lowland wetlands |
| Woodlands |

c)   State **two** characteristics of heaths.

    1:..

    2:..

[2]

[Total 4 marks]

2   Study **Figure 2**, an OS® map of a rural area in the north west of England.

a)   Identify the type of ecosystem found at grid reference 190845.

Figure 2

....

[1]

b)   Give the direction from Strands Bridge to Raylands Wood.

....

[1]

c)   Explain what kind of soils and vegetation you would expect to find in Arnaby Marsh.

....

....

....

....

....

[2]

[Total 4 marks]

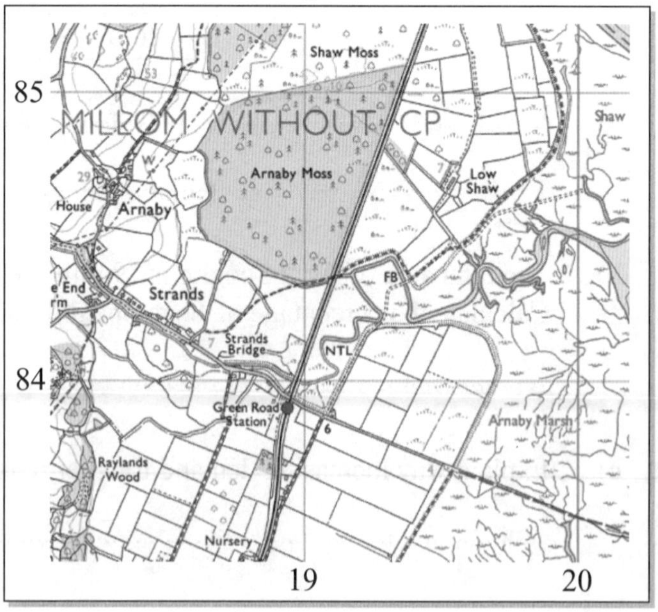

© Crown copyright 2019 OS 100034841

Topic 3 — Ecosystems, Biodiversity and Management

UK Ecosystems

3   **Figure 3** shows the quantity of fish landings (fish caught and brought into a port) in the UK between 1938 and 2017. The UK's marine ecosystems are an important source of fish for food.

a)   Give **two** reasons, other than providing food, why the UK's marine ecosystems are an important resource.

1:...

....

....

2:...

....

....
[2]

Figure 3

(graph: Quantity of fish landings (thousand tonnes) vs Year, 1938 to 2018. Line rises from ~1130 in 1938 to peak ~1230 around 1948, falls to ~920 by 1958, rises to ~1050 around 1968, then declines to ~540 by 1998 and ~490 by 2017.)

b)   Describe the trend of the graph in **Figure 3**.

....

....

....

....
[3]

c)   Suggest how increased demand for fish might have contributed to the trend shown in **Figure 3**.

....

....

....
[2]

d)   Explain **two** other ways in which human activities are degrading marine ecosystems.

1:...

....

....

2:...

....

....
[4]

[Total 11 marks]

Score:

19

Topic 3 — Ecosystems, Biodiversity and Management

Tropical Rainforests

1 Study **Figure 1**, a photograph of an area of tropical rainforest in Myanmar.

a) Using **Figure 1**, identify **two** characteristics of the vegetation in tropical rainforests.

Figure 1

1:..

....

....

....

2:..

....

....

[2]

b) Describe the climate of tropical rainforests.

....

....

....

....

[3]

c) Identify the statement which best describes the soils found in tropical rainforests.

A Soils are deep and nutrient-rich. ⬯

B Leaf litter provides a thin layer of nutrients on the soil surface. ⬯

C Leaf litter takes a long time to decompose. ⬯

D Leaf litter mixes with the soil to form brown earth. ⬯

[1]

[Total 6 marks]

2 **Figure 2** shows a food web for a tropical rainforest.

Suggest how a decrease in the number of banana trees could affect the number of bats in the rainforest.

Figure 2

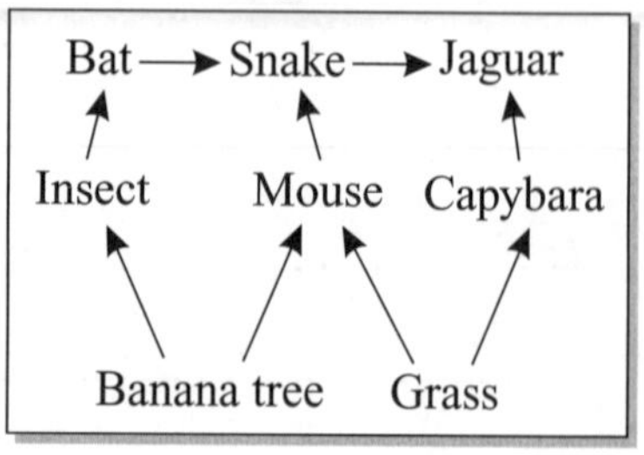

Bat ⟶ Snake ⟶ Jaguar

Insect   Mouse   Capybara

Banana tree   Grass

....

....

....

....

....

....

[Total 2 marks]

Topic 3 — Ecosystems, Biodiversity and Management

Tropical Rainforests

3   Study **Figure 3**, a diagram showing layers of vegetation in a tropical rainforest.

a)   Explain **two** ways that trees in the layer
       labelled A are adapted to their environment.

Figure 3

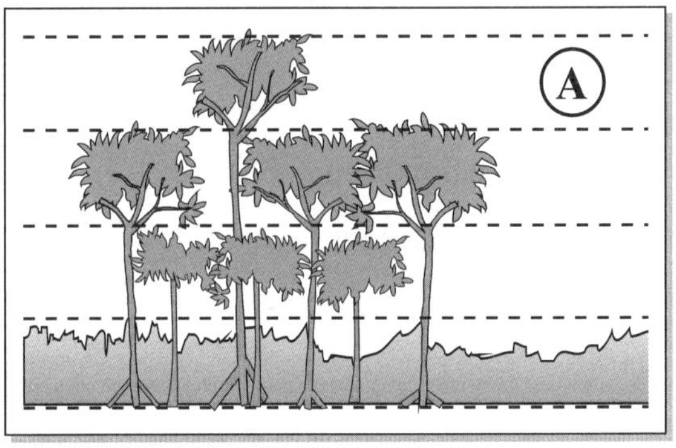

1:...

....

....

2:...

....

....

[4]

b)   Explain **two** ways that animals in tropical rainforests are adapted to their environment.

1:..

....

2:..

....

[4]

[Total 8 marks]

4   Study **Figure 4**, a diagram of an epiphyte in a tropical rainforest. Epiphytes are
       plants that grow on other plants, but which do not obtain nutrients from their hosts.

a)   Suggest **one** reason why epiphytes grow high up in the canopy.

Figure 4

....

....

[1]

b)   Using **Figure 4** and your own knowledge, suggest how epiphytes are
       dependent on other parts of the ecosystem.

....

....

....

....

....

....

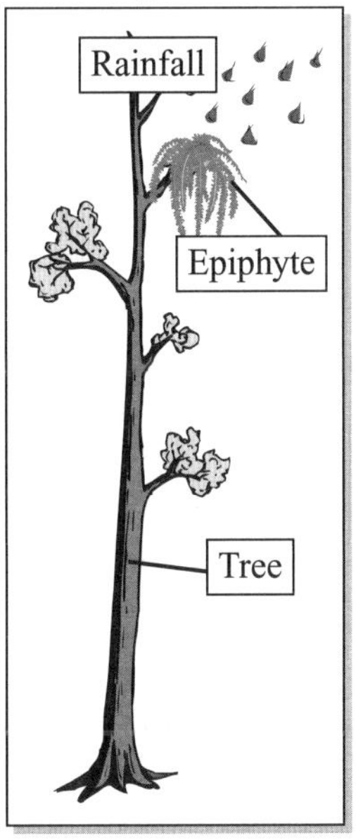

[3]

[Total 4 marks]

Score: _____

20

Tropical Rainforests — Nutrients & Biodiversity

1 Study **Figure 1**, a diagram showing how nutrients are cycled in a tropical rainforest.

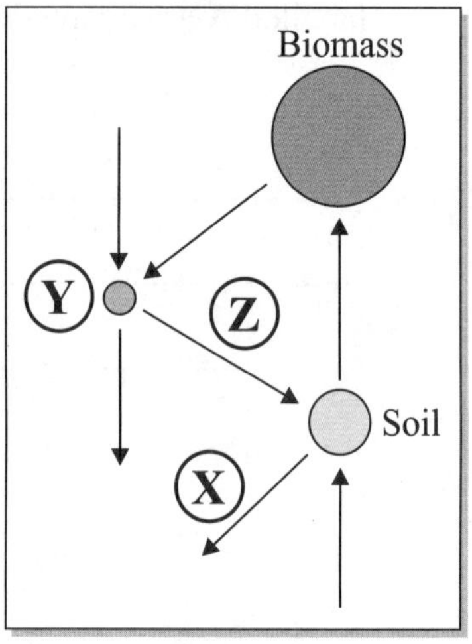

a) Which of the following is the process occurring at the arrow labelled X?

Figure 1

    A   Leaching   ◯

    B   Precipitation   ◯

    C   Surface runoff   ◯

    D   Rock weathering   ◯

[1]

b) Name the nutrient store labelled Y.

....

[1]

c) State the form in which most nutrients in tropical rainforests are stored.

....

[1]

d) Describe how nutrients are transferred along the arrow labelled Z.

....

....

....

[2]

[Total 5 marks]

2 Tropical rainforests have high biodiversity.

a) Define the term 'biodiversity'.

....

....

[1]

b) Explain **one** reason why tropical rainforests have high biodiversity.

....

....

....

[2]

[Total 3 marks]

Score:

8

Topic 3 — Ecosystems, Biodiversity and Management

Tropical Rainforests — Human Uses and Impacts

1 Study **Figure 1**, a series of maps showing the extent of deforestation in an area of tropical rainforest between 1966 and 2016.

Figure 1

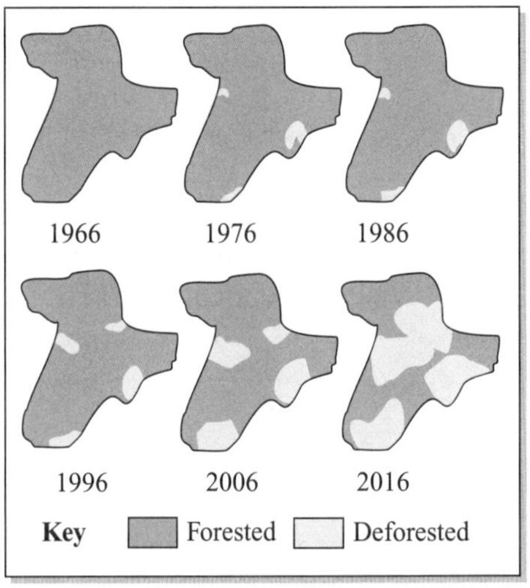

a) Using **Figure 1**, describe the changes to the rainforest between 1966 and 2016.

....

....

....

.... *[2]*

b) State **two** possible reasons for the deforestation of the area shown in **Figure 1**.

1:..

....

2:...

.... *[2]*

c) Suggest why many people consider tropical rainforests to be a valuable resource.

....

....

....

....

.... *[4]*

d) Explain **two** ways in which climate change is a threat to tropical rainforests.

1:...

....

....

2:...

....

.... *[4]*

[Total 12 marks]

Score:

12

Tropical Rainforests — Sustainable Management

1   Study **Figure 1**, a graph showing the number of tourists visiting an area of tropical rainforest.

Always read the axis labels on graphs carefully so you are sure what's being measured and what the units are.

Figure 1

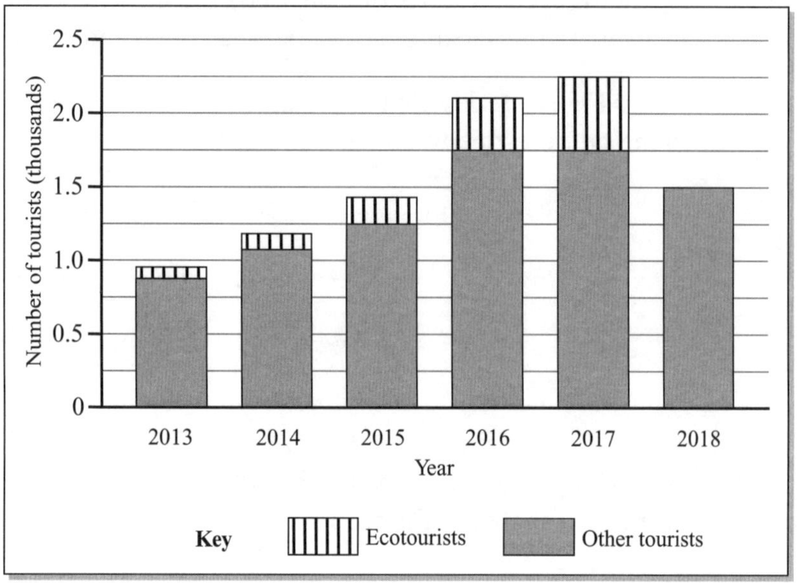

a)   State how many tourists in total visited the area in 2017.

....
[1]

b)   Complete **Figure 1** to show that 750 ecotourists visited in 2018.
[1]

c)   Using **Figure 1**, describe the trend in the number of ecotourists visiting the tropical rainforest.

....

....

....
[2]

d)   Suggest **one** reason for the trend in the number of ecotourists visiting the tropical rainforest.

....

....

....
[2]

e)   Identify **one** advantage of ecotourism.

A   Areas of forest are cleared to make way for new roads.   ◯

B   Commercial logging increases.   ◯

C   Sales of timber increase.   ◯

D   Entrance fees bring in money for rainforest conservation.   ◯
[1]

f)   Assess how political and economic factors contribute to the sustainable management of a tropical rainforest in a named region.

[8 + 4 SPaG]

[Total 19 marks]

Score:

19

Deciduous Woodlands

1   Study **Figure 1**, which shows a deciduous woodland in Essex.

Figure 1

a)   Using **Figure 1**, explain how soils form in
deciduous woodlands.

....

....

....

....

....

....

....

[3]

b)   Describe **two** features of the biotic components of deciduous woodlands.

1:...

....

2:...

....

[2]

c)   Describe the climate of deciduous woodlands.

....

....

....

....

[3]

d)   Suggest how deforestation could affect different components of a deciduous woodland ecosystem.

....

....

....

....

....

[4]

[Total 12 marks]

Deciduous Woodlands

2   Study **Figure 2**, a photograph of beech trees in a deciduous woodlands.

a)   Identify **one** way in which trees are adapted to the
conditions in deciduous woodlands.

Figure 2

A   Broad leaves and wide branches   ⬭

B   Buttress roots   ⬭

C   Thick, waxy leaves with drip tips   ⬭

D   Losing leaves throughout the year   ⬭

[1]

b)   Explain how trees like those shown in **Figure 2** have
adapted to conserve water during the winter.

....

....

....

[2]

Figure 3

c)   Study **Figure 3**, a photograph of a hedgehog.
Explain why hedgehogs and other mammals
in deciduous woodlands hibernate.

....

....

....

....

....

[2]

d)   Explain **two** other ways that animals in deciduous woodlands are adapted to their environment.

1:...

....

....

2:...

....

....

[4]

[Total 9 marks]

Score: ⬜

21

Topic 3 — Ecosystems, Biodiversity and Management

Deciduous Woodlands — Nutrients & Biodiversity

1   Study **Figure 1**, a Gersmehl model of nutrient cycling in a deciduous woodland.

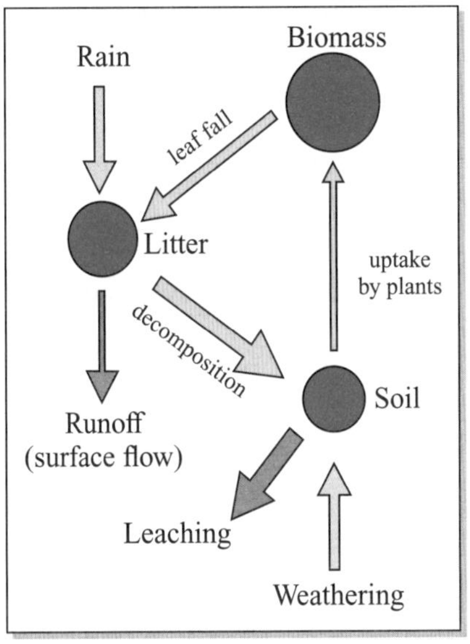

a)   Explain why the soil is a large store of nutrients in deciduous woodlands.

....

....

....

....

....

....

[2]

Figure 1

b)   State **two** possible reasons why nutrient transfers are smaller and slower in deciduous woodlands than in tropical rainforests.

1:...

....

2:...

....

[2]

c)   Suggest how the size of the litter store changes throughout the year.

....

....

....

[2]

d)   Explain **two** reasons why woodlands are moderately diverse ecosystems.

1:...

....

....

2:...

....

....

[4]

[Total 10 marks]

Score: ☐

10

Deciduous Woodlands — Human Uses and Impacts

1 Study **Figure 1**, a photograph of timber extraction in a deciduous woodland.

a) Identify **one** other good or service that people get from deciduous woodlands.

Figure 1

....

....
                                                                    [1]

b) Suggest why demand for timber from deciduous woodlands is increasing.

....

....

....
                                                                                            [2]

[Total 3 marks]

2 Study **Figure 2**, which shows changes in the average annual temperature in a deciduous woodland between 1985 and 2015.

Figure 2

Year	1985	1990	1995	2000	2005	2010	2015
Mean annual temperature (°C)	9.25	9.50	9.75	9.90	10.05	10.10	10.20

a) Calculate the percentage increase in mean annual temperature between 1985 and 2015.

....

....
                                                                                            [1]

b) Suggest **one** way that the pattern of temperature change shown in **Figure 2** could affect the functioning of deciduous woodlands.

....

....

....
                                                                                            [2]

c) Explain **one** other way that climate change could threaten deciduous woodlands.

....

....

....
                                                                                            [2]

[Total 5 marks]

Score:

8

Topic 3 — Ecosystems, Biodiversity and Management

Deciduous Woodlands — Sustainable Management

1   Study **Figure 1** and **Figure 2**, photographs taken in the New Forest,
     an area of deciduous woodland in southern England.

Figure 1   **Figure 2**

a)   i)   Suggest how building footpaths, such as the one shown in **Figure 1**,
            can contribute to the sustainable management of deciduous woodlands.

      ....

      ....
                                                                                                          [2]

      ii) Using **Figure 1**, identify **one** other way in which the New Forest is being managed.

      ....
                                                                                                          [1]

b)   **Figure 2** shows the New Forest Heritage Centre, where visitors can learn about the New Forest.
      State **two** possible ways in which education could contribute to the sustainable management of
      deciduous woodlands.

      1:...

      ....

      2:...

      ....
                                                                                                          [2]

c)   The New Forest is located in an area of high population density in southern England.
      Suggest **one** reason why sustainable management is needed in the New Forest.

      ....

      ....

      ....
                                                                                                          [2]

d)   Assess the effectiveness of different approaches to the sustainable use and management of
      deciduous woodlands in a named region.
                                                                                    [8 + 4 SPaG]
                                                                                    [Total 19 marks]

Score:
19

                 Topic 3 — Ecosystems, Biodiversity and Management

Urbanisation

1　Study **Figure 1**, a graph showing the change in the urban population of more developed countries and less developed countries between 1950 and 2000.

a)　Complete the graph to show that the urban population of less developed countries in 2000 was 2 billion.

[1]

Figure 1

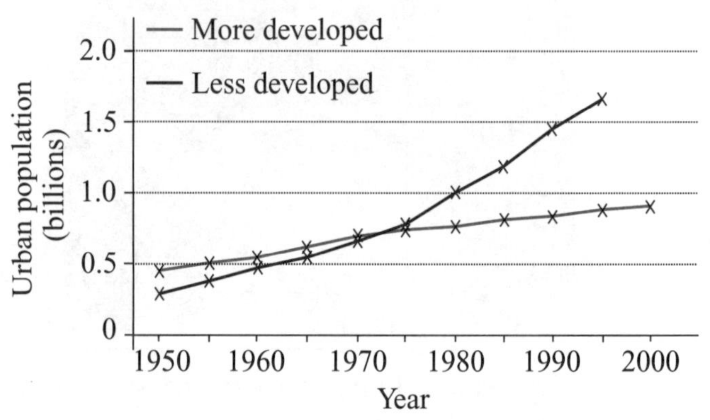

b)　In 1950 the urban population of less developed countries was 0.3 billion. Calculate the percentage change in the urban population between 1950 and 2000.

....

....

....

....

[1]

c)　Describe the trends shown in **Figure 1**.

....

....

....

....

....

[3]

d)　Explain **two** reasons why the rate of urbanisation in developed countries is different to the rate in emerging and developing countries.

1:..

....

....

2:..

....

....

[4]

[Total 9 marks]

Urbanisation

2 **Figure 2** shows a street in the Republic of Ireland, a developed country.

Figure 2

a) Using **Figure 2**, identify **one** effect of urbanisation.

....

....
[1]

b) Explain **one** other effect of urbanisation
on cities in developed countries.

....

....

....
[2]

[Total 3 marks]

3 Study **Figure 3** showing the urban population of the
Democratic Republic of the Congo between 1960 and 2010.

Figure 3

a) Which **one** of the following ways of presenting data would you
select to show the change in urban population in **Figure 3**?

	Urban population (thousands)
1960	3400
1970	4924
1980	7136
1990	10 603
2000	16 534
2010	25 818

   A   Dispersion diagram   ○

   B   Line graph   ○

   C   Pie chart   ○

   D   Population pyramid   ○
[1]

b) Describe **one** social effect of urbanisation in emerging and developing countries.

....

....

....
[2]

c) Describe **one** possible environmental effect of urbanisation in emerging and developing countries.

....

....

....
[2]

[Total 5 marks]

Score: ☐

17

 ☐   ☐   ☐

Urbanisation in the UK

1   Study **Figure 1**, a map showing the population density of the UK.

Figure 1

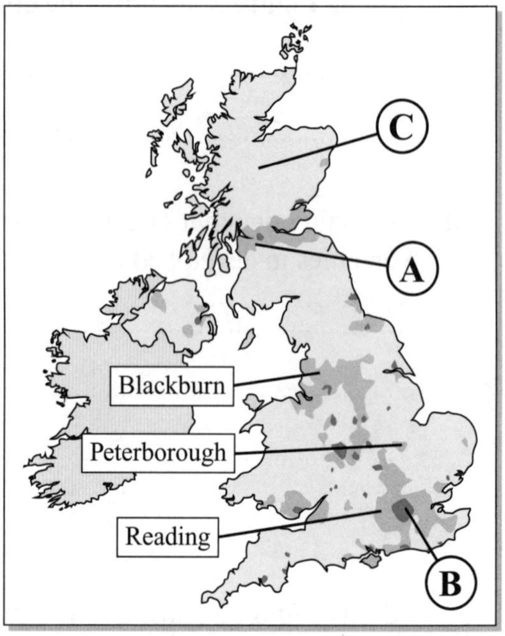

a) i) Use your knowledge of the distribution of urban areas
       in the UK to explain the patterns shown in **Figure 1**.

....

....

....

....
                                                            [2]

   ii) Name the cities labelled A and B in **Figure 1**.

   A: ....

   B: ....
                                                            [2]

  iii) State **one** reason why the area labelled C on
       Figure 1 has no major urban areas.

....
                                                            [1]

   Figure 2 shows some data for three urban areas in the UK.

b) i) Calculate the mean employment rate for
       the three urban areas.

....

....
                                                            [1]

Figure 2

	Blackburn	Peterborough	Reading
Percentage change in population (2008-2017)	+2.7%	+13.0%	+7.7%
Employment rate (2017)	64%	74%	78%
Average weekly earnings (2017)	£493.50	£496.60	£656.70

   ii) Suggest **two** reasons why Reading has
       experienced greater population growth
       than Blackburn.

   1: ....

....

....

   2: ....

....

....
                                                            [4]
                                                   [Total 10 marks]

Score: ☐

10

Urban Change — UK

1 Study **Figure 1**, a photograph of a street in Northern Ireland in an area that has experienced de-industrialisation.

Figure 1

a) i) State what part of the city the street in **Figure 1** is most likely to be found in.

....
[1]

ii) For a UK city you have studied, explain the impacts of de-industrialisation.

....

....

....

....

....

....
[4]

Some people living in cities aim to improve their quality of life by moving to the suburbs.

b) i) Which of the following is **not** usually a factor leading to suburbanisation?

   A   Inner city areas are often overcrowded.   ○

   B   Suburban areas have more green spaces, so quality of life is higher.   ○

   C   Public transport is often good in suburban areas, so commuting is easy.   ○

   D   Suburban areas have many nightclubs and bars, so entertainment is easily accessible. ○
[1]

ii) For a named city in the UK, explain **two** strategies that have been used to improve people's quality of life.

1: ....

....

....

2: ....

....

....
[4]

[Total 10 marks]

Topic 4 — Changing Cities

Urban Change — UK

2   Study **Figure 2**, a map of central Newcastle, a city centre experiencing re-urbanisation.

Figure 2

a)   Give **two** pieces of evidence from **Figure 2** that indicate that the area shown is the CBD.

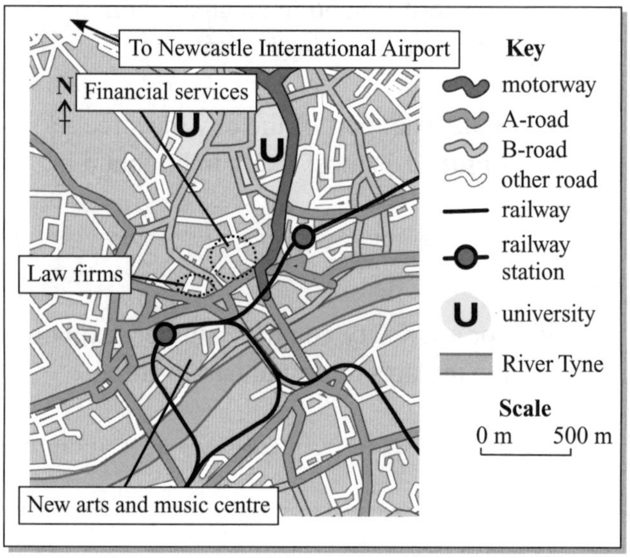

1:..

....

....

2:..

....

....

[2]

b)   Define the term 're-urbanisation'.

....

[1]

c)   Using **Figure 2**, suggest **two** reasons why re-urbanisation has taken place in Newcastle.

1:...

....

2:...

....

[2]

[Total 5 marks]

3   Study **Figure 3**, a graph showing the migration of males into and out of London in 2013 across a range of age groups.

a)   Using **Figure 3**, which age group experienced a net increase in population due to migration?

Figure 3

A   0-10 years   ⬭

B   11-20 years   ⬭

C   21-30 years   ⬭

D   31-40 years   ⬭

[1]

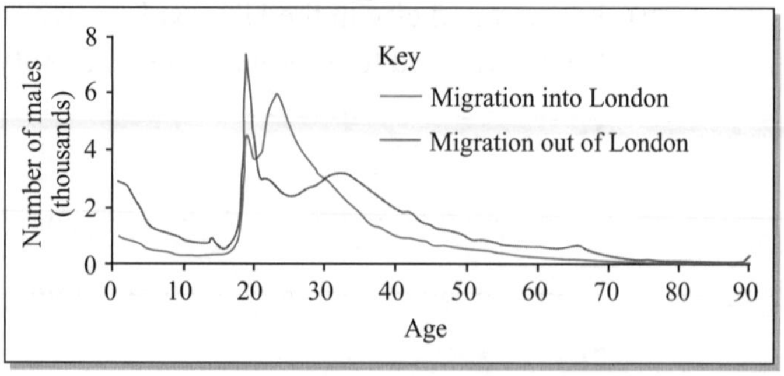

b)   With reference to **Figure 3**, suggest why the population of London is growing.

....

....

....

[2]

Urban Change — UK

c) Explain **one** trend in migration for a named UK city.

....

....

....

[2]

d) For a UK city that you have studied, describe **two** ways in
    which immigration has affected different areas of the city.

    1:..

    ....

    ....

    2:..

    ....

    ....

[4]

[Total 9 marks]

4   Study **Figure 4**, which shows an area of Byrnshire in 1950
    and 2016. Parts of the area have experienced de-centralisation.

Figure 4

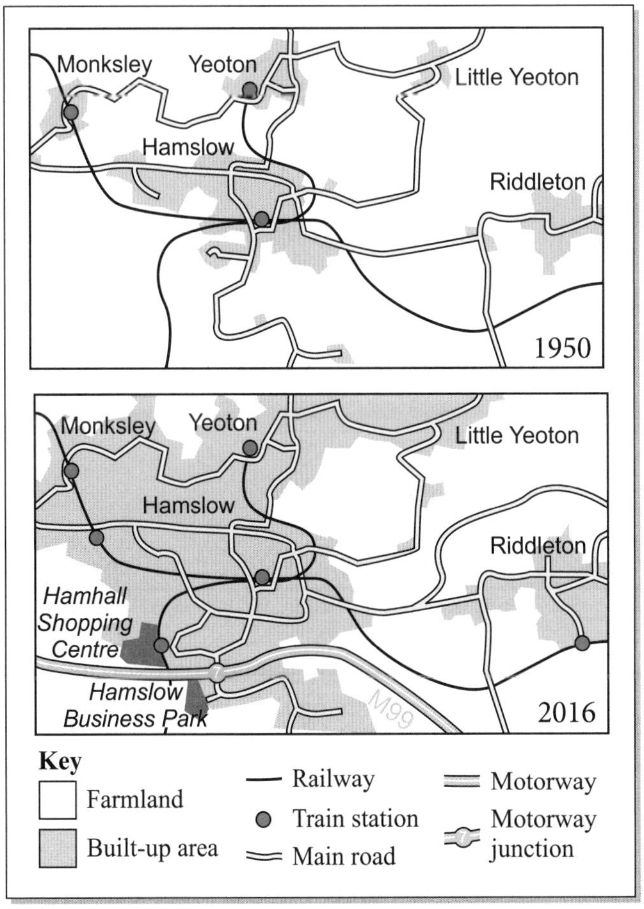

a) Define the term 'de-centralisation'.

    ....

    ....

    ....

    ....

    ....

[1]

b) Study **Figure 4**. Identify **one** piece of
    evidence that shows de-centralisation
    has taken place in this area of Byrnshire.

    ....

    ....

    ....

    ....

    ....

[1]

Urban Change — UK

c) Suggest how developments in transport may have contributed to de-centralisation in Hamslow.

....

....

....

[2]

[Total 4 marks]

5 Study **Figure 5**, a graph showing population change in London from 2004 to 2014, and **Figure 6**, a graph showing house prices and the number of new houses built in London from 2004 to 2016.

Figure 5

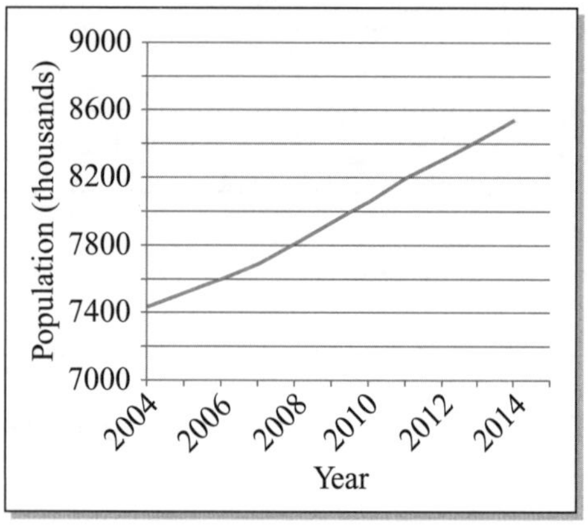

Figure 6

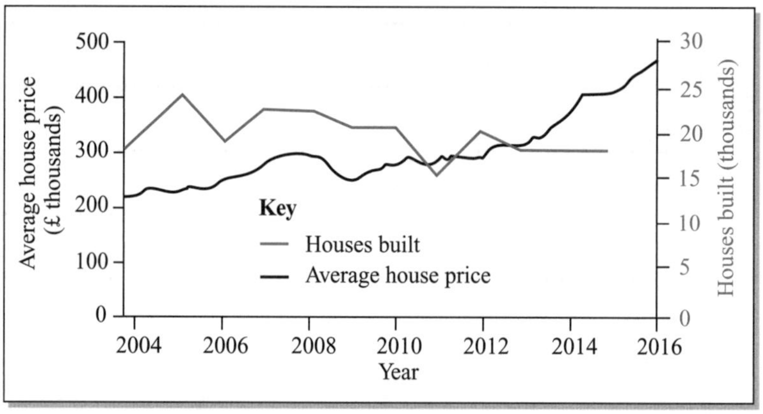

a) Using **Figure 5** and **Figure 6**, suggest why London is facing a housing crisis.

....

....

....

....

[3]

b) Describe **one** way that a named UK city has made some of its housing more sustainable.

....

....

....

[2]

[Total 5 marks]

6 Many cities in the UK are experiencing increasing inequality due to economic change, which is affecting people's quality of life.

For a major city in the UK that you have studied, assess the impact of economic change on quality of life in the city.

[8 + 4 SPaG]

[Total 12 marks]

Score: [   ]

45

Urban Change — Global

1 Study **Figure 1**, a diagram showing land use in a model city in an emerging country. The model shows where commercial, residential and industrial areas are likely to be found.

a) Label the diagram in **Figure 1** to show where the oldest parts of the city are likely to be found.

[1]

Figure 1

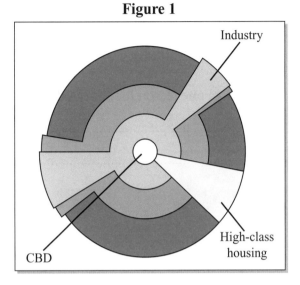

b) Identify the part of a city where rapid growth is most likely to be taking place.

....
[1]

c) Identify the part of a city where high density low-quality housing is most likely to be found.

....
[1]

d) Suggest **one** reason for the location of industry in **Figure 1**.

....

....

....
[2]

[Total 5 marks]

2 Study **Figure 2**, a photograph of some students in a city in Indonesia, an emerging country. Some emerging countries are rapidly urbanising.

a) Using **Figure 2** and your own knowledge, suggest **two** reasons why people might leave rural areas to move to a city in a developing or emerging country.

1:...

....

....

....

....

2:...

Figure 2

© iStock Editorial / Getty Images Plus

....

....
[2]

Urban Change — Global

Natural increase and international migration can also lead to rapid urbanisation in emerging countries such as Indonesia.

b) State how natural increase leads to population growth.

....

....

[1]

c) Give **one** reason for increased international migration to cities in emerging countries.

....

....

[1]

[Total 4 marks]

3 Study **Figures 3** and **4**, photos of two different areas of a city in an emerging country.

Figure 3

Figure 4

a) Suggest why there are big differences in quality of life within cities in emerging and developing countries.

....

....

....

....

[4]

b) Explain how the government are attempting to improve the quality of life in a named city in an emerging or developing country.

....

....

....

....

....

[4]

[Total 8 marks]

Urban Change — Global

4   Study **Figure 5**, a photo of a squatter settlement in a city in an emerging country.

a)   i)   Define the term 'squatter settlement'.

Figure 5

....

....

....

.... *[1]*

   ii) Explain **two** challenges for people living
        in squatter settlements.

   1: ....

   ....

   ....

   ....

   2: ....

   .... *[4]*

   iii) Describe **one** challenge other than squatter settlements caused by the rapid growth of cities in
        emerging countries.

   ....

   ....

   .... *[2]*

   Top-down and bottom-up strategies are being used to improve the quality of life
   for residents of squatter settlements.

b)   i)   State **one** disadvantage of bottom-up strategies being used to improve quality of life in cities.

   ....

   .... *[1]*

   ii) For a named city in an emerging or developing country, assess the effectiveness of
        top-down and bottom-up strategies that have been used to improve quality of life.

[8 + 4 SPaG]

[Total 20 marks]

Score:

37

Topic 4 — Changing Cities

Measuring Development

1   Study **Figure 1**, which shows measures of development for Canada, Malaysia and Angola.

a)   Identify which of the following is a measure of economic development.

Figure 1

	Canada	Malaysia	Angola
GDP per capita	$46 705	$29 449	$6644
Birth rate	10.2	18.8	43.7
Life expectancy	82.0	75.4	60.6
Gini coefficient	34.0	41.0	42.7
HDI value	0.926	0.802	0.581

A   GDP per capita   ◯

B   Birth rate   ◯

C   Life expectancy   ◯

D   Gini coefficient   ◯
                                        [1]

b)   Calculate the range of birth rates in **Figure 1**.

....

....
                                                                                                                [1]

c)   Explain why the Human Development Index (HDI) values given in **Figure 1** may be a better measure of development than any of the other measures.

....

....

....
                                                                                                                [2]

d)   Explain **one** political indicator that can be used to determine the level of development in a country.

....

....

....

....
                                                                                                                [3]

e)   Explain which of the countries shown in **Figure 1** is the most developed.

....

....

....

....

....
                                                                                                                [4]

                                                                                        [Total 11 marks]

Score:

11

Global Development

1   Study **Figure 1**, an article about Libya written in 2018.

Figure 1

Libya is the fourth largest country in Africa. It is located on the northern edge of the Sahara desert. More than 90% of the country is a desert or semi-desert environment.

Libya was an Italian colony for much of the early 20th century until it was captured and occupied by Allied forces during the Second World War. Libya declared independence in December 1951.

Since gaining independence, Libya has suffered from periods of poor international relations and conflict. It currently ranks 108th out of 189 countries in terms of human development.

a)   i)   Using **Figure 1**, explain how climate may have affected the level of development of Libya.

....

....

....

....
[3]

    ii)   Explain **one** other physical factor that can affect how developed a country is.

....

....

....
[2]

b)   Identify **two** economic factors that can affect the level of a country's development.

1:...

2:...
[2]

c)   Explain how being a former colony may affect a country's economic development.

....

....

....

....
[3]

[Total 10 marks]

Score: ☐

10

UK Development

1   Study **Figure 1**, a map showing how life expectancy for males varies across the UK.

a)   Describe how life expectancy for males varies across the UK.

Figure 1

....

....

....

....
[2]

b)   Give **one** example, other than life expectancy,
of an indicator of uneven development in the UK.

....
[1]

[Total 3 marks]

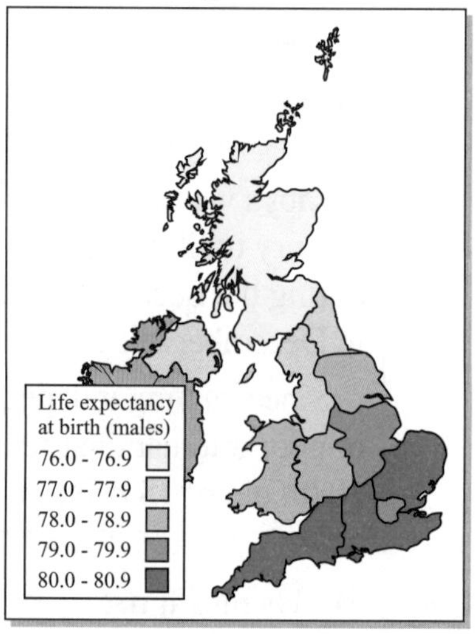

2   Study **Figure 2**, photographs of Chadderton, a northern town, and Bath, a southern city.

Figure 2

a)   Using **Figure 2**, identify **one** piece of evidence for inequality within the UK.

....

....
[1]

b)   Explain **two** reasons for uneven development in the UK.

1:..

....

2: ....

....
[4]

[Total 5 marks]

Score: ☐

8

Effects of Uneven Development

1   Study **Figure 1**, which shows development data for Haiti (a developing country) and the UK (a developed country). The table includes data on housing, health and food security.

a)   Define the term 'food security'.

....

....

....

....

....
                                 [1]

Figure 1

	Haiti	UK
Population living in slums (% of urban population)	74.4	No data
Infant mortality rate (deaths of children aged 0-12 months per 1000 live births)	53.9	3.7
Hospital beds (per 1000 people)	0.7	2.8
Access to improved sanitation	27.6%	99.2%
Undernourishment	45.8%	2.5%

b)   With reference to **Figure 1**, describe the impact of uneven development on the availability and condition of housing in different parts of the world.

....

....

....

....
                                                                    [3]

c)   Using **Figure 1**, suggest how uneven development might have consequences for the health of people in developing countries.

....

....

....

....

....
                                                                    [4]

d)   Explain how a lack of development affects education and employment in developing countries.

....

....

....

....

....
                                                                    [4]

[Total 12 marks]

Score: ☐

12

Increasing Development

1   Development projects can be described as 'top-down' or 'bottom-up'.

a)   Identify the statement which best describes 'bottom-up' development projects.

     A   Strategies where transnational corporations direct projects designed to increase development with little or no input from local communities.   ⬭

     B   Strategies which usually use high-tech equipment and machinery, often operated by skilled workers from developed countries.   ⬭

     C   Strategies funded by governments or companies to aid development with the aim of generating profit.   ⬭

     D   Strategies where local people and communities decide on ways to improve things for their own community.   ⬭

[1]

b)   Describe **one** type of international strategy to increase development.

....

....

....

....

[3]

c)   State **two** advantages of development projects being led by local communities.

1:..

....

2:..

....

[2]

d)   Explain the disadvantages of 'top-down' strategies for the country where they are taking place.

....

....

....

....

....

[4]

[Total 10 marks]

Score:

10

Developing and Emerging Countries

1 Study **Figure 1**, which shows the contributions of primary industry, secondary industry and services to the total GDP of an emerging country.

a) Complete **Figure 1** to show that secondary industry contributed 30% to the total GDP in 2016. *[1]*

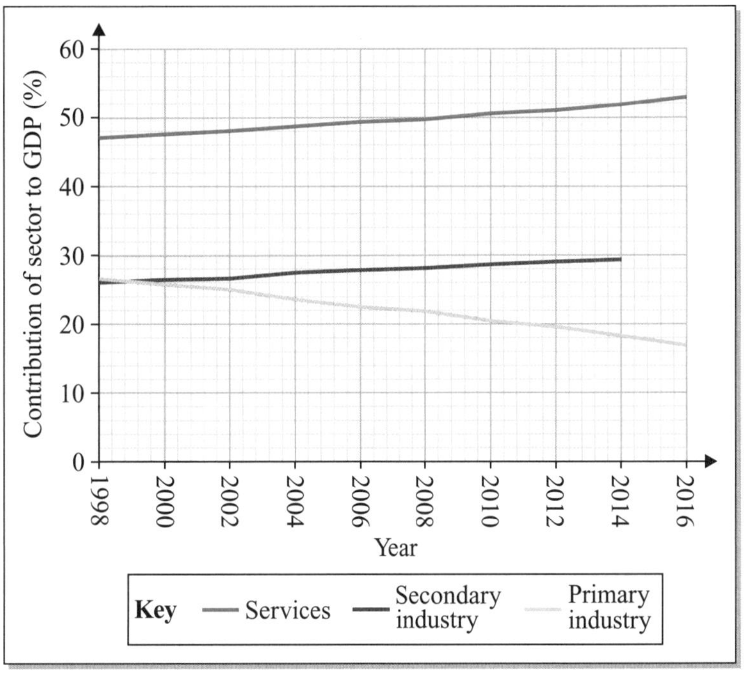

b) The country's total GDP in 2016 was US$ 1.9 trillion. Calculate the amount of GDP contributed by primary industry in 2016 in US$. Show your working.

....
[2]

Figure 1

c) State **one** example of a primary industry.

....
[1]

d) State **one** potential advantage and **one** potential disadvantage of the changes that have occurred in the different economic sectors shown in **Figure 1**.

Advantage:...

....

Disadvantage: ....

....
[2]

e) For an emerging or developing country you have studied, describe its involvement in international trade.

....

....

....

....
[3]

[Total 9 marks]

Topic 5 — Global Development

Developing and Emerging Countries

2   Study **Figure 2**, which shows population pyramids for a country in 1980 and 2010.

a)   Compare the population pyramids for 1980 and 2010.

....

....

....

....

....

....

....

[3]

Figure 2

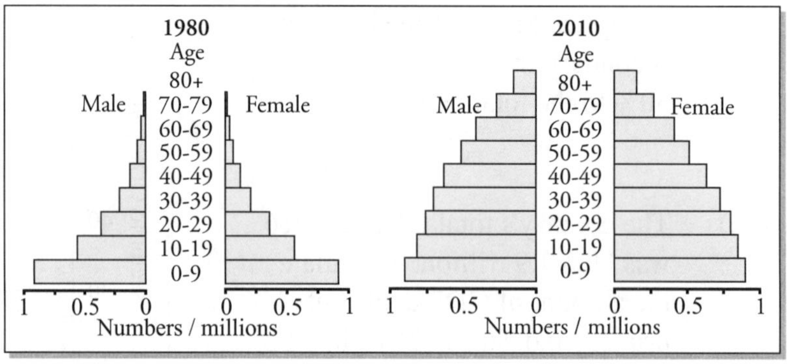

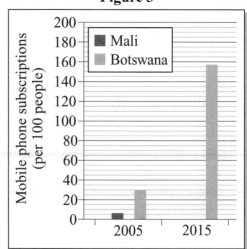

b)   Explain **two** reasons for the changes in population structure shown in **Figure 2**.

1:...

....

2:...

....

[4]

[Total 7 marks]

3   **Figure 3** shows how mobile phone subscriptions changed between 2005 and 2015 in Mali (a developing country) and Botswana (an emerging country).

a)   Complete **Figure 3** to show that the mobile phone subscriptions in Mali in 2015 were 130 per 100 people. *[1]*

b)   Calculate the increase in mobile phone subscriptions in Botswana between 2005 and 2015.

....

....

[1]

Figure 3

c)   Suggest **one** reason for the increase in mobile phone subscriptions shown in **Figure 3**.

....

....

....

[2]

Developing and Emerging Countries

d)   For an emerging or developing country that you have studied, explain **one** way
     that an increase in the use of technology has affected people there.

     ....

     ....

     ....
                                                                                                                         [2]

e)   'Increasing inequality is the most important social change occurring in emerging and
     developing countries.' Assess this statement using examples from an emerging or
     developing country that you have studied.
                                                                                                                         [8]
                                                                                                      [Total 14 marks]

4   Study **Figure 4**, which shows the yearly level of foreign private
       investment in a region of an emerging country between 2008 and 2016.

                                                                                    Figure 4

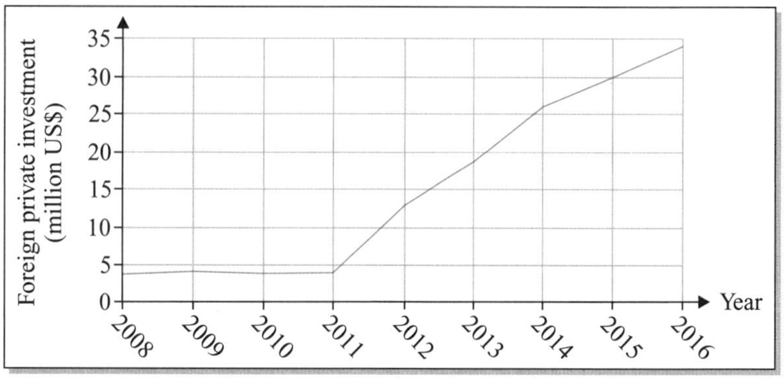

a)   Using **Figure 4**, describe how foreign
     private investment in the region
     changed between 2008 and 2016.

     ....

     ....

     ....

     ....

     ....
                                                                                                                         [2]

b)   i)   Explain the role of transnational corporations (TNCs) in the development
          of an emerging or developing country that you have studied.

          ....

          ....

          ....

          ....

          ....
                                                                                                                         [4]

     ii) For a named emerging or developing country that you have studied, explain **one** way
          that the government's foreign policy has affected the country's development.

          ....

          ....

          ....
                                                                                                                         [2]
                                                                                                      [Total 8 marks]

Developing and Emerging Countries

5   Study **Figure 5**, which shows development data for four different regions of a developing country. Two of the regions are part of the core and two are part of the periphery.

a)   Identify the **two** regions that are most likely to be part of the periphery.

Figure 5

Region	A	B	C	D
Infant mortality rate (per 1000 live births)	34	15	11	31
Literacy rate (%)	63	87	91	69
GDP per capita (US$)	686	2201	2507	798

A   A and D   ◯

B   A and B   ◯

C   B and C   ◯

D   B and D   ◯

[1]

b)   Suggest **one** reason for the regional variation in GDP per capita.

....

....

....

[2]

c)   Suggest why literacy rate varies between the regions in **Figure 5**.

....

....

....

[2]

d)   For a named emerging or developing country, explain **two** strategies that the government is using to improve people's quality of life.

1:..

....

....

2:..

....

....

[4]

e)   Evaluate the positive and negative impacts of rapid development on the people in an emerging or developing country that you have studied.

[8 + 4 SPaG]

[Total 21 marks]

Score: ☐

59

Natural Resources

1   Natural resources can be classified in different ways.

a)   Name **two** abiotic natural resources.

    1:..

    2:..
                                                                                                    [2]

b)   Identify which of these statements about renewable resources is true.

    A   Renewable resources can be replenished on a short timescale.   ⬭

    B   Renewable resources take millions of years to form.   ⬭

    C   Coal and natural gas are renewable resources.   ⬭

    D   Renewable resources are often extracted from the ground.   ⬭
                                                                                   [1]

c)   Exploiting natural resources can have negative environmental impacts.
    State **one** environmental impact of mining for coal.

    ....

    ....
                                                                                                    [1]

d)   Extracting water resources may involve building dams.
    State **one** way in which building dams can reduce biodiversity.

    ....

    ....
                                                                                                    [1]
                                                                                          [Total 5 marks]

Figure 1

2   Study **Figure 1**, a photograph of farmland in southern Scotland.

a)   Explain **one** way that farming can contribute
    to a reduction in biodiversity.

    ....

    ....

    ....
                                                                                                    [2]

b)   State **one** way that farming can cause soil erosion.

    ....

    ....
                                                                                                    [1]
                                                                                          [Total 3 marks]

Score: ☐

8

 ☐   ☐   ☐

UK Distribution of Resources

1 Study **Figure 1**, an Ordnance Survey® map showing an area in Wales used to generate hydro-electric power.

Figure 1

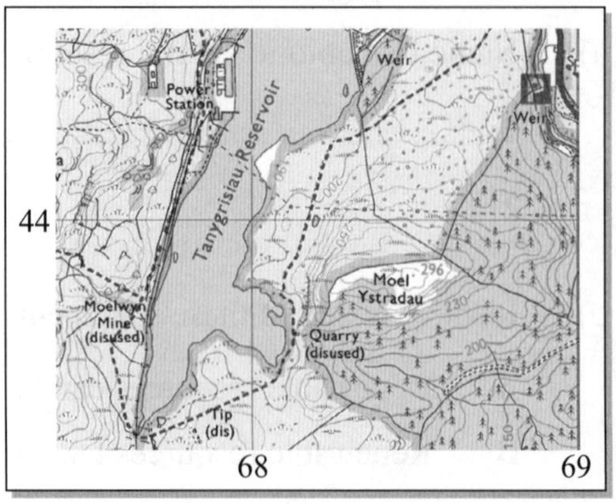

© Crown copyright 2019 OS 100034841

a) State the four-figure grid reference of the power station.

....
[1]

b) Suggest **one** reason why this area is suitable for hydro-electric power generation.

....

....

....
[2]

c) Identify **two** natural resources, other than water, shown in **Figure 1**.

1:..

2:..
[2]

[Total 5 marks]

2 Study **Figure 2**, which shows the distribution of different types of farming in the UK.

Figure 2

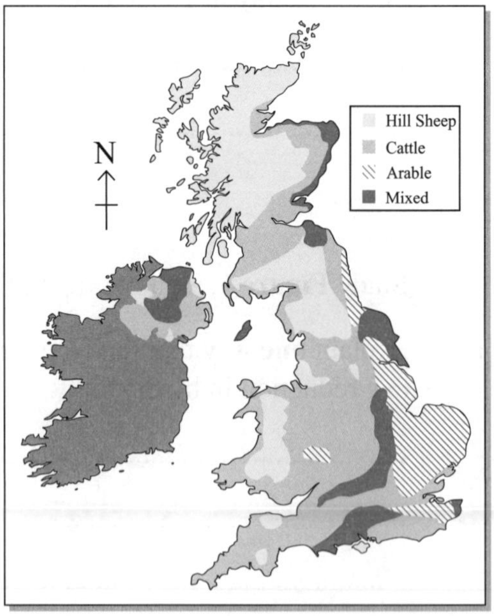

a) Using **Figure 2**, describe the distribution of hill sheep farming in the UK.

....

....

....

....

....
[2]

Hill Sheep
Cattle
Arable
Mixed

N

b) Suggest **one** reason for the distribution of arable (crop) farming shown in **Figure 2**.

....

....

....
[2]

[Total 4 marks]

Score:

9

Topic 6 — Resource Management

Global Distribution & Consumption of Resources

1   Resources are distributed unevenly around the world.

a)   Identify the statement about the global distribution of forestry resources which is **not** correct.

    A   Canada and Russia have large areas of forest which are exploited for timber.   ◯

    B   Logging occurs in tropical forests in South America and west Africa.   ◯

    C   South Africa is the world's biggest producer of timber.   ◯

    D   There are forestry resources in northern Europe.   ◯

[1]

b)   Give **one** reason why global agricultural resources are unevenly distributed.

....

....
[1]

[Total 2 marks]

2   Study **Figure 1**, which shows the oil consumption and production of several countries in 2014.

a)   i)   Using **Figure 1**, identify which country had the lowest oil production in 2014.

    ....
[1]

Figure 1

ii) Using **Figure 1**, state how much oil Russia produced in 2014.

    ....

    ....
[1]

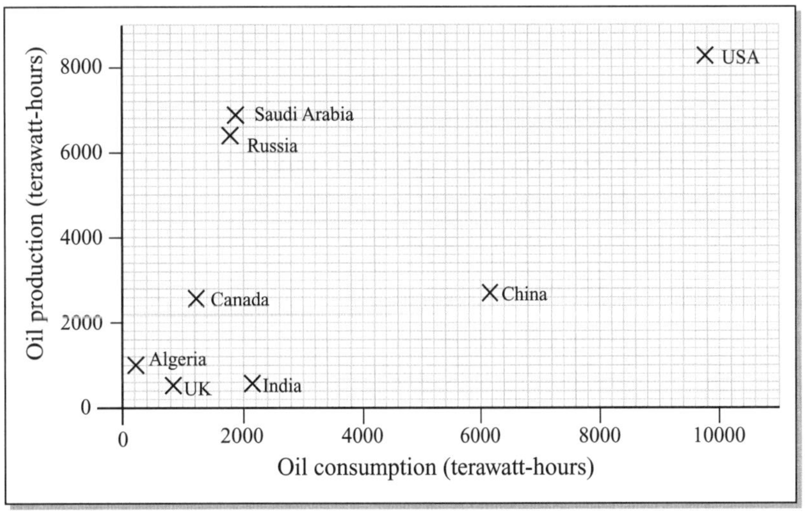

iii) Explain which country in **Figure 1** needed to import the most oil resources in 2014.

....

....

....
[2]

b)   Explain **one** reason why some countries consume more energy than others.

....

....

....
[2]

[Total 6 marks]

Topic 6 — Resource Management

Global Distribution & Consumption of Resources

3 Study **Figure 2**, which shows information about the GDP and annual rainfall of several countries.

Figure 2

	Brazil	Chile	Namibia	Australia	UK
GDP per head (US $)	12 027	14 794	5393	62 328	46 783
Average annual rainfall (mm)	1761	1522	285	534	1220

a) Calculate the mean rainfall for the countries shown in **Figure 2**.

....

[1]

b) Chile uses a greater percentage of its available water resources than Brazil does.
Using **Figure 2**, suggest **two** reasons for this.

1:..

....

2:..

....

[4]

[Total 5 marks]

4 Study **Figure 3**, which shows average daily calorie intake per person around the world.

a) Using **Figure 3**, identify which **one** of the statements below is correct.

A Daily calorie intake is lower in Country A than in Country C. ◯

B Daily calorie intake in Country B is 3095 to 3265 kcal. ◯

C Daily calorie intake in Country A is 3266 to 3357 kcal. ◯

D Daily calorie intake is highest in Country C. ◯ *[1]*

Figure 3

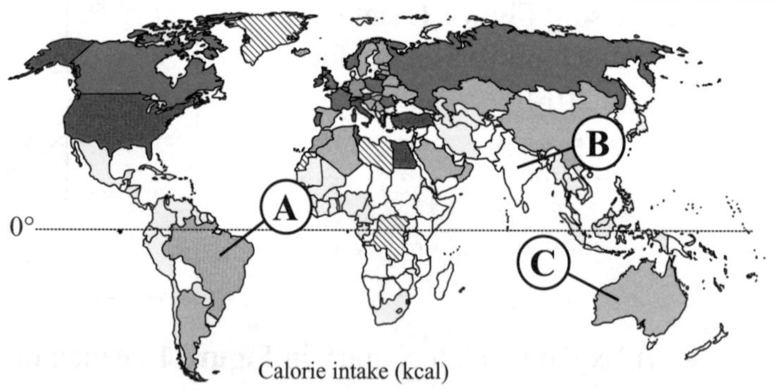

Calorie intake (kcal)
- ■ Over 3539
- ■ 3358 to 3539
- ■ 3266 to 3357
- ■ 3095 to 3265
- □ 2546 to 3094
- □ Less than 2546
- ▨ No data available

b) Suggest **one** reason for the difference in daily calorie intake between Country B, an emerging country, and Country C, a developed country.

....

....

....

[2]

[Total 3 marks]

Score: ☐

16

Meeting Energy Demand

1 Study **Figure 1**, a photograph showing an oil drilling facility in Alberta, Canada. Oil is a non-renewable energy resource.

Figure 1

a) Define the term 'non-renewable energy resource'.

....

.... *[1]*

b) Suggest **one** advantage of using oil as an energy resource.

....

....

.... *[2]*

[Total 3 marks]

2 Increasing wealth has contributed to an increase in global energy demand. Some countries are responding to increasing demand for energy by developing nuclear energy or by fracking.

a) Give **one** reason why increased wealth has contributed to an increase in global energy demand.

....

.... *[1]*

b) Explain **one** disadvantage of producing nuclear power.

....

....

.... *[2]*

c) i) Describe the process of fracking.

....

....

....

.... *[3]*

ii) Explain how fracking could help to resolve energy shortages in the future.

....

....

.... *[2]*

[Total 8 marks]

Meeting Energy Demand

3 Study **Figure 2**, a map of Barmouth Bay, Wales.

a) State which location, A-E, would be the best site for an onshore wind farm. Give **one** reason for your choice.

Location:...
[1]

Reason: ....

....

....

....
[1]

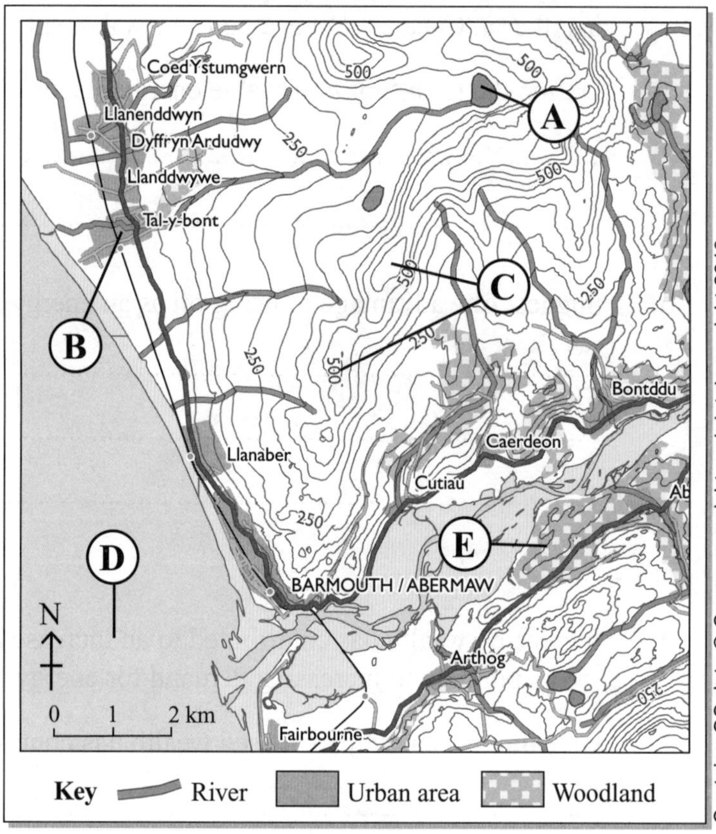

Contains OS data © Crown copyright and database right 2019

Figure 2

Key — River | Urban area | Woodland

b) Give **one** way in which building a solar power plant at location E could negatively affect the environment.

....

....

....
[1]

c) Give **one** objection that people might have to the development of a wind farm.

....

....
[1]

d) For a renewable energy resource you have studied, explain **two** advantages of using this resource to increase energy supply.

1:...

....

....

2:...

....

....
[4]

[Total 8 marks]

Score:

19

The Energy Mix

1 Study **Figure 1**, pie charts showing UK's energy mix in 1970 and 2014.

a) State which source of energy
the UK most relied on in 1970.

....
[1]

Figure 1

Key
- Coal
- Oil
- Gas
- Nuclear
- Wind/Hydro
- Biofuels

1970: 6%, 3%, 44%, 47%

2014: 2%, 6%, 7%, 17%, 34%, 34%

b) State which energy source increased its
share the most between 1970 and 2014.

....
[1]

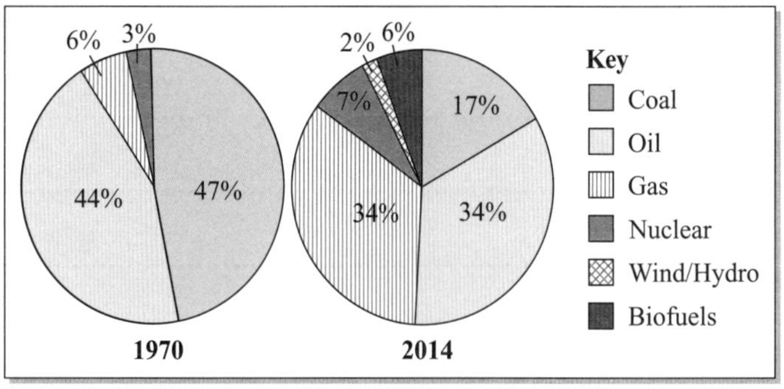

c) Using **Figure 1**, compare the UK's energy mix in 1970 and in 2014.

....

....

....

....
[3]

d) i) The changes in energy sources shown in **Figure 1** are similar in many developed countries.
Give **two** possible reasons why increasing wealth can lead to a country's energy mix using a
smaller proportion of fossil fuels.

1: ....

....

2: ....

....
[2]

ii) Explain how population growth can affect a country's energy mix.

....

....

....
[2]

iii) State **one** other factor, besides wealth and population growth,
which can affect a country's energy mix.

....

....
[1]

[Total 10 marks]

Score:

10

Sustainable Energy Management

1   Study **Figure 1**, a photograph of a coal-fired power station in the UK.

a)   State **two** opinions that individuals might have towards the exploitation of the energy resource shown in **Figure 1**.

Figure 1

1:...

....

....

2:...

....

....
[2]

b)   Attitudes towards the sustainable management of energy resources vary with different stakeholders.
     i)   Define the term 'sustainable energy management'.

     ....

     ....
     [1]

     ii)   State **one** reason why energy resources need to be managed.

     ....

     ....
     [1]

c)   Explain the view of **two** stakeholder groups, other than individuals,
     who would support using more renewable energy resources in the future.

     1:..

     ....

     ....

     2:..

     ....

     ....
     [4]

d)   Using examples from named countries with different levels of development, assess how a
     country's sustainable energy management strategies are affected by its level of development.

     [8 + 4 SPaG]

     [Total 20 marks]

     Score: ☐

     20

Global Water Distribution and Consumption

1 Study **Figure 1**, which shows water use in an emerging country in 1998 and 2018.

a) Identify the proportion of water withdrawals
   for domestic purposes in 2018.

   A   84%   ◯

   B   16%   ◯

   C   24%   ◯

   D   5%   ◯
                              [1]

Figure 1

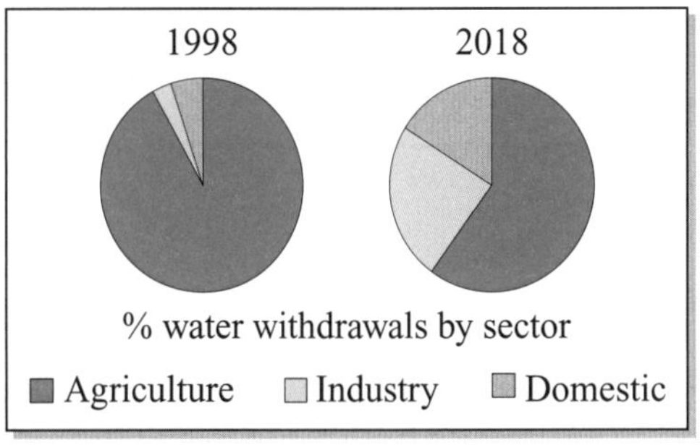

1998   2018

% water withdrawals by sector
■ Agriculture ▨ Industry ▨ Domestic

b) Suggest **one** reason for the change in water withdrawals for industry between 1998 and 2018
   shown in **Figure 1**.

   ....

   ....

   ....
                                                                                                        [2]

                                                                                          [Total 3 marks]

2 Study **Figure 2**, information about water resources in North America.

a) Identify the country with the lowest
   average rainfall.

   ....
                              [1]

b) Using **Figure 2**, suggest **one** reason
   why Mexico has a water deficit.

   ....

   ....

   ....

   ....
                              [2]

Figure 2

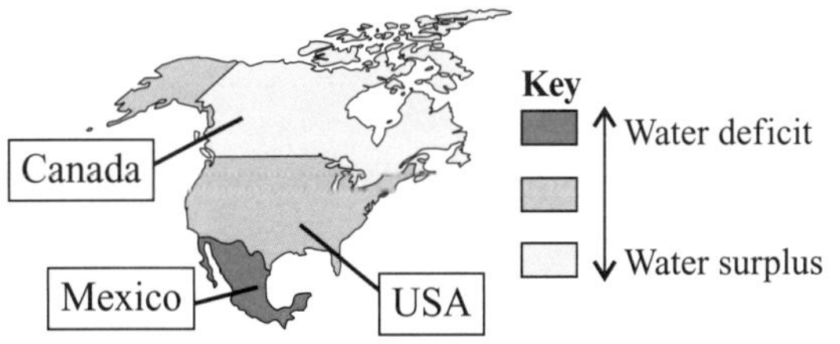

Key
■ Water deficit
▨
□ Water surplus

Canada

Mexico   USA

	USA	Canada	Mexico
Average rainfall (mm)	715	537	758
Average temperature (°C)	9.2	−2.6	20.9
Population density (people per km²)	35	4	65
Water consumption per person (m³ per year)	1630	1130	750

c) Using **Figure 2**, suggest why Canada has a water surplus.

   ....

   ....

   ....

   ....
                                                                                                        [3]

Global Water Distribution and Consumption

d) Explain how climate change has decreased the water supply in some parts of the world.

....

....

....

[2]

[Total 8 marks]

3 Study **Figure 3**, which shows water withdrawals per capita in two countries between 1990 and 2018.

Figure 3

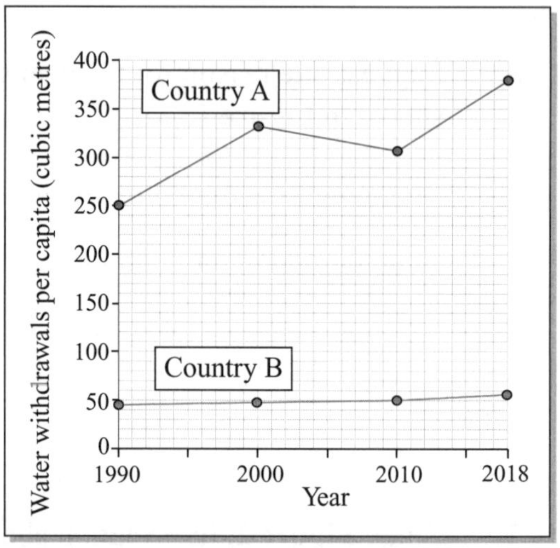

a) Calculate the difference in water withdrawals per capita between Country A and Country B in 2005.

....

[1]

b) Calculate the percentage increase in water withdrawals per capita in Country A between 1990 and 2018.

....

[1]

c) Country A is an emerging country. Suggest **two** reasons for the overall increase in water use per capita in Country A between 1990 and 2018, shown in **Figure 3**.

1:..

....

....

2:..

....

....

[4]

d) Explain **one** piece of evidence from **Figure 3** that indicates that Country B is a developing country.

....

....

....

[2]

[Total 8 marks]

Score:

19

Water Supply Problems

1 Supplying enough water to parts of the UK can be a challenge.

a) Explain **one** reason why there are water supply problems in the UK.

....

....

....
[2]

b) Explain how reservoirs can help overcome imbalances in water supply and demand.

....

....

....
[2]

[Total 4 marks]

2 Study **Figure 1**, a photo showing children collecting water in Kenya, Africa.

a) Give **one** piece of evidence from **Figure 1** that indicates that this area has water supply problems.

Figure 1

© iStock Editorial / Getty Images Plus

....

....

....

....
[1]

b) Using **Figure 1**, give **one** impact of water supply problems on the people in this community.

....

....
[1]

c) Explain **one** reason why emerging and developing countries often have water supply problems.

....

....

....
[2]

[Total 4 marks]

Score:

8

Topic 6 — Resource Management

Exploiting Water Resources

1   Study **Figure 1**, which shows information about water resources in Algeria.

Figure 1

Approximate values based on World Bank data	1970	1980	1990	2000	2010
Total annual freshwater withdrawals (billion cubic meters)	2.00	3.00	4.44	5.60	7.39
Renewable internal freshwater resources per capita (cubic metres)	760	580	437	360	318

a)   Calculate the difference in renewable internal freshwater resources
per capita between 1970 and 2010.

....
[1]

b)   Calculate the median volume of freshwater withdrawn in Algeria between 1970 and 2010.

....
[1]

c)   Explain **one** concern that the government of Algeria might have
about the supply and consumption of water resources.

....

....

....
[2]

d)   Compare the attitudes that individuals and businesses might have towards
the exploitation and consumption of water resources in Algeria.

....

....

....

....
[3]

e)   Explain how technology could help resolve water shortages in Algeria.

....

....

....
[2]

[Total 9 marks]

Score:

9

Sustainable Water Management

1   Study **Figure 1**, a diagram showing domestic water supply and use in a developed country.

a)   Using **Figure 1**, explain how individuals
are attempting to manage water resources
in a sustainable way.

....

....

....

....

....

....

....

....
[3]

Figure 1

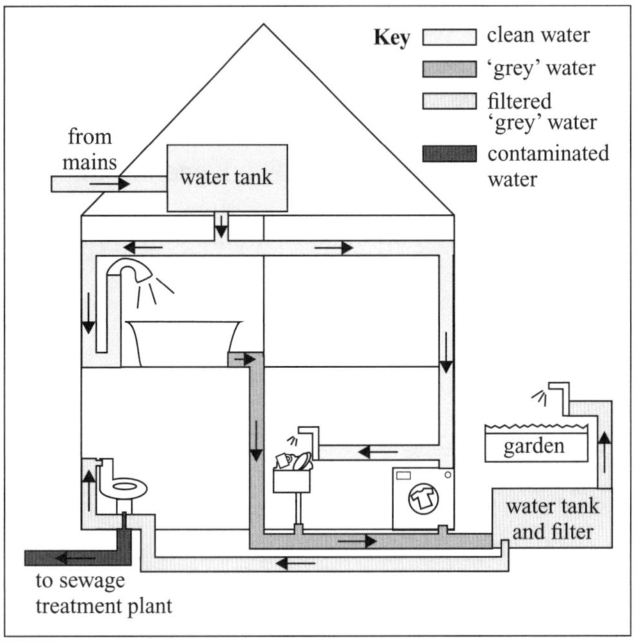

Key
- clean water
- 'grey' water
- filtered 'grey' water
- contaminated water

from mains → water tank

garden

water tank and filter

to sewage treatment plant

b)   Describe the attitudes that **two** different stakeholder groups might have
about how to manage water resources sustainably.

1:..

....

....

2:..

....

....
[4]

c)   Suggest **one** reason why there may need to be international co-operation between the
governments of different countries to make sure that water resources are managed sustainably.

....

....

....
[2]

d)   Using examples from **two** countries at different levels of development,
examine the strategies used in an attempt to manage water resources sustainably.

[8 + 4 SPaG]

[Total 21 marks]

Score: ☐

21

Fieldwork in a Physical Environment

1   You have carried out fieldwork in **either** a river **or** coastal environment.

You might not have completed your fieldwork yet — don't start this section until your enquiry is finished.

Name your river/coastal environment fieldwork location.

....

a)   Explain how your fieldwork enquiry improved your understanding of an area of geography.

....

....

....

....

[3]

b)   i)   Describe **one** of the quantitative data collection techniques that you used.

....

....

....

[2]

ii)   Explain how **one** of your quantitative data collection techniques was appropriate to the task.

....

....

....

....

[3]

c)   i)   Describe **one** of the qualitative data collection techniques that you used to record the landforms that make up the river/coastal landscape.

....

....

....

[2]

ii)   Explain **one** limitation of using the data collection technique that you described in part i).

....

....

....

[2]

Fieldwork in a Physical Environment

d) Explain **two** strengths of **one** of the data presentation techniques that you used.

Data presentation technique:..

1:...

....

....

2:...

....

....

[4]

e) Explain **one** way that the use of maps was helpful in your investigation.

....

....

....

[2]

f) Explain how **one** of the statistical techniques you used to analyse your data helped you to draw conclusions in your investigation.

....

....

....

[2]

g) Explain **one** way that the river/coastal processes in the landscape that you studied have affected the people living in the area.

....

....

....

....

[3]

h) Assess the extent to which your results allowed you to reach a valid conclusion to your original question.

[8]

[Total 31 marks]

Score:

31

Investigating River Landscapes

1 As part of a fieldwork enquiry into river landscapes, a student collected data on river discharge. He began by measuring the river velocity. The student placed a float in the river and recorded the time taken for the float to travel 10 metres downstream. The results are shown in **Figure 1**.

If you studied coasts for your fieldwork enquiry you don't need to answer these questions — there are questions about coasts on the next page.

Figure 1

Sample	Time (s)
1	315
2	255
3	278
4	310
5	947
6	302
7	279
8	297

a) Give **one** appropriate item that could be used as the float. Give a reason for your answer.

Item:..
[1]

Reason: ....

....

....
[1]

b) The result for sample 5 is an anomaly.
Suggest **one** possible reason for the anomaly.

....

....

....
[2]

c) Excluding the anomaly, calculate the **median** time taken for the float to travel 10 m.

....

....

Median = ... s
[1]

d) Excluding the anomaly, calculate the **mean** time taken for the float to travel 10 m.

....

....

Mean = ... s
[1]

e) Describe **one** source of qualitative data that the student could collect as part of his enquiry.

....

....

....
[2]

[Total 8 marks]

Score:

8

Investigating Coastal Landscapes

1   A student wanted to investigate how wave characteristics affect the cross-profile of a beach.
Figure 1 shows the method she used to find the cross-profile of the beach. She measured
the profile at three points along the beach. The results are shown in **Figure 2**.

Figure 1

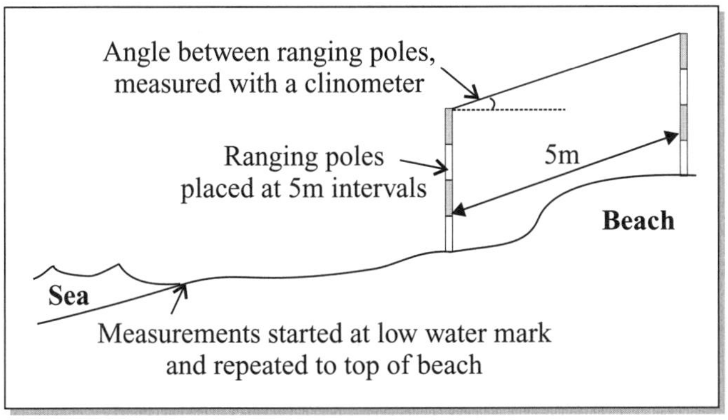

Angle between ranging poles,
measured with a clinometer

Ranging poles
placed at 5m intervals

5m

Beach

Sea

Measurements started at low water mark
and repeated to top of beach

Figure 2

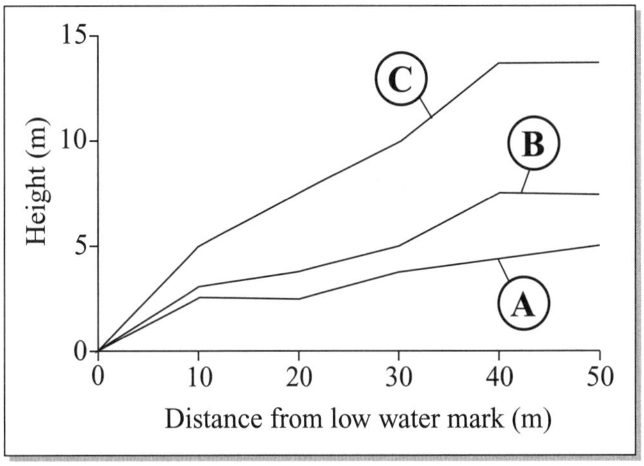

Height (m) — vertical axis: 0, 5, 10, 15

Distance from low water mark (m) — horizontal axis: 0, 10, 20, 30, 40, 50

Curves labelled C, B, A

a)   Explain **two** possible sources of inaccuracy in the method used.

1:...

....

2:...

....

[4]

b)   Suggest how the student might have chosen the points along the beach at which to measure
the cross-profiles.

....

....

[2]

c)   Suggest **one** way in which the student could add to **Figure 2** so that the data is presented
more effectively.

....

....

[2]

d)   Explain **one** way in which the reliability of the data could be improved.

....

....

[2]

[Total 10 marks]

Score:

10

Fieldwork in a Human Environment

1   You have carried out fieldwork investigating change in **either** an urban **or** a rural area.

Name your urban/rural environment fieldwork location.

....

a)   Explain why you used **one** of the primary data collection techniques involved in your enquiry.

Primary data collection technique:..

Explanation:...

....

....

[2]

b)   Explain which sampling technique (e.g. random, stratified or systematic) was best suited to your investigation.

....

....

....

[2]

c)   Explain **two** ways in which you managed the risks associated with your fieldwork.

1:...

....

2:...

....

[4]

d)   You used census data in your investigation. Explain how this data source was useful.

....

....

....

[2]

Fieldwork in a Human Environment

e)   Other than the data you collected, suggest **one** source of data that
     would have helped you to answer your original question.

     ....

     ....

     ....
     [2]

f)   Explain how you used **one** of your data presentation techniques to show your results effectively.

     ....

     ....

     ....
     [2]

g)   Explain **one** limitation of your data presentation methods.

     ....

     ....

     ....
     [2]

h)   Explain how collecting data on the quality of the environment allowed you to reach conclusions
     about how the area you studied has changed over time.

     ....

     ....

     ....

     ....

     ....

     ....
     [4]

i)   Evaluate the suitability of the sites you chose for data collection.
     [8]

     [Total 28 marks]

     Score:

     28

Investigating Changing Urban Areas

1 A student is investigating whether the physical landscape affects land use within the CBD and inner city areas of Suninsky. Part of her enquiry involves recording the primary land use in different parts of the city. The locations of her sampling sites, A-F, are shown in **Figure 1**. The student's results are shown in **Figure 2**.

Only do this page if your enquiry was about urban areas — the next page covers rural areas.

Figure 1

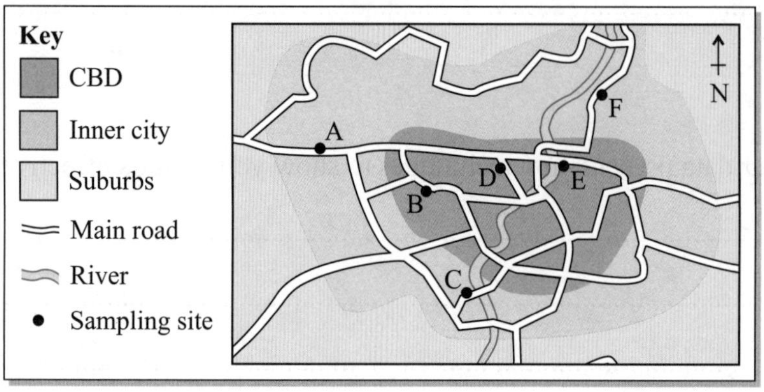

Key
- ■ CBD
- □ Inner city
- □ Suburbs
- ～ Main road
- ～ River
- • Sampling site

Figure 2

Location	Land Use
A	Medium-class residential
B	High-class residential
C	Commercial/Industrial
D	Commercial
E	Commercial
F	Low-class residential/Industrial

a) i) Explain **one** reason why the student's choice of sampling sites is suitable for this investigation.

....

....

....
[2]

ii) Suggest **one** way in which the student could have increased the validity of the investigation.

....

....

....
[2]

b) State **one** secondary data source that could be used to support this investigation.

....
[1]

c) With reference to **Figure 1** and **Figure 2**, suggest **one** conclusion that the student might have drawn from her investigation.

....

....

....
[2]

[Total 7 marks]

Score: ☐

7

Geographical Investigations — Fieldwork

Investigating Changing Rural Areas

1 Some students investigated how changes in land use have affected the quality of the rural environment surrounding their school. They carried out interviews at several sites by asking pedestrians a series of questions. The questions that the students asked are shown in **Figure 1**.

Figure 1

Interview Questions
1. What are the best things about the local environment?
2. Which areas of the local environment do you feel could be improved?
3. How would you recommend improving the problems in the local environment?
4. Which local environmental issue do you feel is the most important?

a) Explain **one** possible limitation of using this data collection method.

....

....

....

[2]

b) Suggest **one** way that some of the data from the interviews could be presented.

....

....

....

[2]

c) State **one** other primary data collection method that could be used in this investigation.

....

[1]

d) Explain **one** way that secondary data could be used to support the investigation.

....

....

....

[2]

[Total 7 marks]

Score: ☐

7

Geographical Investigations — UK Challenges

The UK faces challenges around the use of its natural resources and the need to balance the protection of ecosystems against demand for resources. There are debates over how to manage the UK's National Parks — whether to develop them for tourism and resource extraction, or to focus more on conservation.

Figure 1: Location of the UK's National Parks

1 Cairngorms
2 Loch Lomond and the Trossachs
3 Northumberland
4 Lake District
5 Yorkshire Dales
6 North York Moors
7 Peak District
8 Snowdonia
9 Broads
10 Pembrokeshire Coast
11 Brecon Beacons
12 Dartmoor
13 Exmoor
14 New Forest
15 South Downs

Figure 2: Facts about tourism and the UK economy

Value of tourism to the UK economy in 2014	£127.4 billion
Predicted value of tourism to the UK economy in 2025	£257.4 billion
Jobs in tourism, 2014	2.97 million
% of the UK's total tourist spending that was spent in rural areas, 2014	15%

Figure 3: Visitor spend and number of visitors in 2014 to the top five most-visited National Parks in the UK

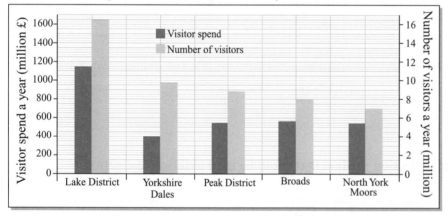

Figure 4: Condition of the main habitats in designated Sites of Special Scientific Interest (SSSIs) in Dartmoor National Park

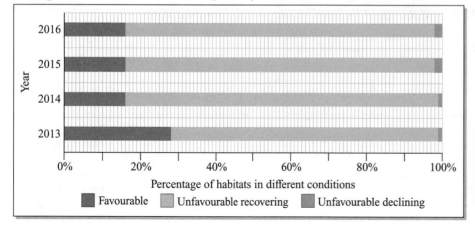

Figure 5: Facts about National Parks

Cairngorms National Park is home to 25% of the UK's threatened wildlife species.

It is estimated that 10 million tonnes of carbon are stored in the peat bogs of Dartmoor National Park.

In 2017, volunteers in Loch Lomond and the Trossachs National Park cleared an area of invasive rhododendron plants equivalent to three football pitches.

In 2018, researchers at the University of East Anglia found that spending time outdoors and living close to nature can reduce people's risk of developing health problems such as stress and high blood pressure.

Geographical Investigations — UK Challenges

Figure 6: Photographs of human impacts on Dartmoor National Park

Footpath erosion

Litter collected from a disused quarry

Figure 7: Information about the populations of National Parks and the population of England and Wales

	Lake District	New Forest	North York Moors	Peak District	England and Wales
Population	40 261	35 278	22 997	37 247	58 744 595
Population density (people per km²)	18	64	16	26	389
% aged 65 and over	29.3	31.7	30.0	28.3	18.2
Median age	52.5	54.1	53.7	52.5	39.9

Figure 8: Challenges for communities in rural areas

RURAL NEWS

MARCH 2017

RURAL AREAS STRUGGLING TO ACCESS SERVICES

A report by the Local Government Association and Public Health England has shown that people in rural areas often struggle to access jobs and important services like schools and health care. The average journey time by public transport or walking to a hospital is less than 40 minutes in urban areas, but closer to an hour in rural areas. This is especially serious for the 14% of rural households which don't own a car. When asked to comment on the report's findings, a local resident said, "The problem is that we just don't have the infrastructure in this area — it's a difficult balance between developing the facilities needed by local people and making sure we protect wildlife and the natural landscape".

Figure 9: Proposals for development in National Parks

Woodsmith Mine
North York Moors National Park

- Plan to build a mine to extract polyhalite (a mineral used to make agricultural fertiliser) and a 37 km tunnel to transport the polyhalite to a processing plant.
- Planning permission granted.

Exbury solar farm
New Forest National Park

- Proposal for a 22 hectare solar farm, near the Lepe Loop recreational route.
- Planning permission refused.

Affordable homes — Cairngorms National Park

- Proposal to build 46 houses in two villages in the Cairngorms National Park, including social housing provided by the Highland Council for people on low incomes.
- Planning permission granted.

Geographical Investigations — UK Challenges

1   Study **Figure 1**, a map showing the location of the UK's National Parks,
and **Figure 2** and **Figure 3**, which show information about tourism in the UK.

a)   Which of the following statements about the locations of the UK's National Parks is correct?

      A   Most of the UK's National Parks are found in Scotland.   ◯

      B   Exmoor National Park is on the coast.   ◯

      C   Two of the UK's National Parks are located in Northern Ireland.   ◯

      D   The New Forest National Park is located in the north of England.   ◯

                            [1]

b)   i)   Using **Figure 2**, calculate the predicted percentage increase in the value of tourism to the
UK economy between 2014 and 2025.

      ....

                            [1]

   ii)   Calculate the range for the number of visitors to the National Parks shown in **Figure 3**.

      ....

                            [1]

  iii)   Calculate the mean annual spend per visitor to the Yorkshire Dales National Park in 2014.

      A   £63.50   ◯

      B   £41.03   ◯

      C   £210   ◯

      D   £32.35   ◯

                            [1]

c)   Using **Figures 1–3** and your own knowledge, explain how developing tourism in National Parks
could help to address the income gap between the south-east and the rest of the UK.

      ....

      ....

      ....

      ....

                            [3]

                      [Total 7 marks]

2   **Figure 4** shows information about the condition of protected habitats in Dartmoor National Park.

      Describe how the proportion of SSSI habitats in favourable condition
changed between 2013 and 2016.

      ....

      ....

      ....

                      [Total 2 marks]

Geographical Investigations — UK Challenges

3 Study **Figure 5**, which shows facts about UK National Parks, and **Figure 6**, which shows photographs of the impacts of visitors on a National Park.

a) Suggest **one** reason why protecting National Parks can reduce the UK's contribution to climate change.

....

....

....

[2]

b) Using **Figure 6**, explain how population increase can put pressure on ecosystems in National Parks.

....

....

....

[2]

[Total 4 marks]

4 **Figures 7**, **8** and **9** show information about populations and development in National Parks.

a) Calculate the mean percentage of the population of the National Parks shown in **Figure 7** that is aged 65 or older.

....

[1]

b) Using **Figure 7**, compare the age and density of the UK's National Parks' populations with those of England and Wales.

....

....

....

....

[3]

c) Using **Figure 8** and **Figure 9**, give **one** reason why local people might be in favour of development in National Parks, and **one** reason why local people might be against it.

1:..

....

2:..

....

[2]

d) Discuss the view that National Parks should be developed for tourism. Use information from **pages 96-97** and your knowledge from the rest of the course to support your answer.

[12 + 4 SPaG]

[Total 22 marks]

Score:

35

Acknowledgements

Geological map of the UK on page 4 from the British Geological Survey ©UKRI; UK fish landings data used to construct graph on page 45 © Crown copyright; employment rate and average weekly earnings in Blackburn, Peterborough and Reading on page 58 source: Centre for Cities. Contains data from the Office for National Statistics; percentage change in population in Blackburn and Reading on page 58 and map of population density in the UK on page 58 source: Office for National Statistics; data for pie charts showing UK's energy mix on page 81 © Crown copyright; value of tourism to the UK economy in 2014 on page 96 source: Office for National Statistics, The Blue Book: 2015 Edition; jobs in tourism data in Figure 2 on page 96 source: Office for National Statistics © Crown copyright 2016; census data for National Parks in Figure 7 on page 97 source: Office for National Statistics. All contain public sector information licensed under the Open Government Licence v3.0. http://www.nationalarchives.gov.uk/doc/open-government-licence/version/3/

Photograph on p.5 (Hound Tor) © John Phillips / p.6 (Newlands Valley) © Richard Webb / p.6 (Meandering River Wampool) © Simon Ledingham / p.10 (Fernycombe Point) © Hugh Venables / p.14 (Waves break on the groyne, West Wittering) © Rob Farrow / p.18 (river landform (interlocking spurs)) © Anne Burgess / p.20 (Gully, Gleann Diomham) © Richard Webb / p.25 (Red Tarn and Helvellyn) © Gareth James / p.26 (Cwm Afon Dudonyn) © GP Williams / p.26 (Lochan a'Choire) © Dave Moir / p.27 (The Three Sisters, Glencoe) © Sylvia Duckworth / p.29 (Quarry, Whitelee Forest) © Richard Webb / p.51 (Layer Wood, Layer Marney) © Roger Jones / p.54 (Timber stacks beside track in Bentley wood) © David Martin / p.55 (Track through Frame Heath Enclosure) © E Gammie / p.55 (New Forest Visitor Centre at Lyndhurst) © Peter Facey / p.57 (Traffic in Ireland) © Albert Bridge / p.59 (Street in Northern Ireland) © Albert Bridge / p.75 (Crop sprayer getting ready) © Oliver Dixon / p.82 (Fiddler's Ferry Power Station) © William Starkey. Licensed under the Creative Commons Attribution-Share Alike 2.0 Generic Licence. http://creativecommons.org/licenses/by-sa/2.0/

Map extracts on pages 7, 12, 17, 25, 44 & 76 reproduced with permission from Ordnance Survey® © Crown copyright 2019 OS 100034841

Data used to compile the UK average rainfall map on page 34 from the Manchester Metropolitan University.

Drought map on page 39 from Aqueduct Global Maps 2.1 Indicators. Constructing Decision-Relevant Global Water Risk Indicators by Francis Gassert, Paul Reig, Tien Shiao, Matt Luck, Research Scientist, ISciences LLC and Matt Landis Research Scientist, ISciences LLC - April 2015. Licensed under a Creative Commons Attribution International 4.0 Licence. https://creativecommons.org/licenses/by/4.0/

Source used to produce the map of UK Ecosystems on page 44: copyright rests with the European Commission; Acknowledgement: Produced by the University of Leicester, The Centre for Landscape and Climate Research and Specto Natura and supported by Defra and the European Environment Agency under Grant Agreement 3541/B2012/RO-GIO/EEA.55055 with funding by the European Union. This resource is made available under the terms of the Open Government Licence v3.0. http://www.nationalarchives.gov.uk/doc/open-government-licence/version/3/.

Graph of world urban population on page 56 from Annual Urban Population at Mid-Year, by UN Population Division, © 2019 United Nations. Reprinted with the permission of the United Nations. https://esa.un.org/unpd/wup/DataQuery/

Democratic Republic of the Congo Urban Population data in table on page 57: © United Nations, Department of Economic and Social Affairs, Population Division (2018). World Urbanization Prospects: The 2018 Revision, Online Edition; Human Development Index values on page 66 from 2015 Human Development Report, United Nations Development Programme from hdr.undp.org. Licensed under the Creative Commons Attribution 3.0 IGO licence. http://creativecommons.org/licenses/by/3.0/igo/

Graph of migration to and from London on page 60 adapted from data from the Office for National Statistics; graph of housing completions on page 62 based on DCLG live table on house building 253; graph of average house prices on page 62 and life expectancy map on page 68 source: Office for National Statistics. Licensed under the Open Government Licence v.3.0. http://www.nationalarchives.gov.uk/doc/open-government-licence/version/3/

Map of central Newcastle on page 60 contains OS data © Crown copyright and database right 2019.

Graph of population of London on page 62 source: Office for National Statistics licensed under the Open Government Licence v2.0. http://www.nationalarchives.gov.uk/doc/open-government-licence/version/2/

GDP data on page 66 source: The World Bank: GDP per capita, PPP (current international $); Gini coefficient data on page 66 source: The World Bank: Development Research Group; oil production and consumption data used in Figure 1 on page 77 source: Vaclav Smil (2017). Energy Transitions: Global and National Perspectives. & BP Statistical Review of World Energy. From Our World in Data; GDP data for 2014 on page 78 source: The World Bank: GDP per capita (current US$); Algeria water use data in Figure 1 on page 86 source: Food and Agriculture Organization, AQUASTAT DATA from The World Bank: World Development Indicators. Licensed under the Creative Commons Attribution 4.0 International Licence (CC BY 4.0). https://creativecommons.org/licenses/by/4.0/legalcode

Birth rates and life expectancies for Canada, Angola and Malaysia on page 66 Source: The World Factbook: Washington, DC: Central Intelligence Agency, 2019.

Photo of Chadderton on page 68 by Jeremy Sutcliffe licensed under the Creative Commons Attribution 2.0 Generic licence. https://creativecommons.org/licenses/by/2.0/deed.en

Photo of Bath on page 68 by AngryGrandpaTheMovie licensed under the Creative Commons Attribution-Share Alike 4.0 International licence https://creativecommons.org/licenses/by-sa/4.0/legalcode

Percentage of Haiti's urban population living in slums on page 69 source: UN HABITAT from The World Bank: World Development Indicators; infant mortality rates for Haiti and the UK on page 69 source: UN Inter-agency Group for Child Mortality Estimation from The World Bank: World Development Indicators; undernourishment data for Haiti and the UK on page 69 source: Food and Agriculture Organization from The World Bank: World Development Indicators; access to improved sanitation data and hospital bed data for Haiti and the UK on page 69 source: World Health Organization (2015) from Our World in Data; mobile phone subscription data used in Figure 3 on page 72 source: International Telecommunication Union, World Telecommunication/ICT Development Report and database from The World Bank; average annual rainfall data in Figure 2 on page 78, average rainfall data in Figure 2 on page 83, population density data in Figure 2 on page 83 source: Food and Agriculture Organization from The World Bank: World Development Indicators. Licensed under the CC-BY 4.0 Licence. https://creativecommons.org/licenses/by/4.0/

Map showing daily calorie intake on page 78 constructed with data from FAO. FAOSTAT. Food Balance Sheets. (Latest update: 2013). Accessed 2019/03/15. URI: http://www.fao.org/faostat/en/?#data/FBS/visualize

Map of Barmouth Bay on page 80 by David Maliphant. Contains OS data © Crown copyright and database right 2019.

Map of water security in North America on page 83 source: World Resources Institute, Water Stress by Country 2013. Licenced for reuse under the Creative Commons Attribution 4.0 International (CC BY 4.0) https://creativecommons.org/licenses/by/4.0/

Data for water consumption per person (m³ per year) on page 83 © Central Intelligence Agency

Value of tourism to the UK economy in 2025 on page 96 source: Oxford Economics.

Data used in Figure 3 on page 96 from National Parks UK.

Data used in Figure 4 on page 96 from Your Dartmoor © Natural England copyright. Contains Ordnance Survey data © Crown copyright and database right 2017.

With thanks to John Howell for permission to use the images on page 97.